Volumes One and Two of the Stronach stories compounded the
popularity of North-east Scotland's most notorious village and
the bizarre array of inhabitants who call it home. Already,
Stronach's fame has reached the US, Canada, Australia,
New Zealand, South Africa, Ireland and beyond.

Now here is Volume Three. Inside, the villagers let slip one or
two secrets as they guide you round their favourite haunts; a
travel journalist visits and compiles a report for a radio holiday
programme; there is a further selection of the best stories from
the first 200 of the Press and Journal Saturday episodes; we have
a new full-length story of intrigue and rivalry at the Stronach
Emporium and General Stores, as well as more mouthwatering
recipes from the ladies of Stronach WRI.

D1537683

Published by **Stronach Media Ltd.**,
Tullynessle, Alford, Aberdeenshire, AB33 8QN

© Stronach Media Ltd.
ISBN  1  897672  04  7

First edition  :  November, 1994

Printed in Scotland by BPC-AUP, Aberdeen

Cover artwork by Susan Bell

**<u>DEDICATION</u>**
**For my mother and father**

# Stronach

## Volume Three

Stronach Media Ltd

# Contents

## STORE WARS

## THE RECIPES

## FAREWELL

# *Foreword*

NEARLY eight years ago, when the Press and Journal began printing episodes every Saturday from the daily life of a small North-east community called Stronach, the newspaper received two standard queries continually. They were dressed up in many different forms, but all boiled down to the same two things.

The first was: "Who writes it?"

The second was: "Where do you get all your ideas?"

I can understand the curiosity about the first. Unusually for a feature in a daily paper, we had taken the decision not to use a by-line; that is, we had decided not to attach the author's name to the work. "Is it because you're embarrassed?" I can remember one correspondent quipping. "Not in the least," we wrote back, "but you can imagine how the villagers of Stronach would react once they knew who was revealing their secrets on a week-to-week basis." It is to the extreme credit of all the people who wrote that they took these replies in the spirit in which they were intended.

Fending these queries put me in a rather difficult position for, as Features Editor at the time, I was the one responsible for providing answers to all these puzzled letters knowing that, wearing another hat, I was the one responsible for sparking the queries in the first place. This is a very difficult balancing act, believe me. It fairly challenges the morals to answer straight questions in such a way that you are not telling lies, but you are also not giving the game away.

Anyway, I am convinced, looking back, that it was this shroud of mystery which helped to establish Stronach as a success very early on. Clearly, people understood from almost the very beginning that Stronach is a real community, which explains why many letters arrived (and still arrive) at the Press and Journal building in Aberdeen addressed to one inhabitant of Stronach or another. One follower of Stronach activities carries on a regular correspondence with Geneva Brose about home baking.

I have recounted already, in the foreword to *Stronach: Volume One*, how we decided early on at the Press and Journal that the series would run its course to 60 episodes and then stop. When it stopped, however, we were inundated with protests and had little choice but to continue.

It was not until September of 1992 that the truth broke. For the five years until then, the authorship of Stronach was pretty much an open secret within the Press and Journal building, but was guarded jealously out and about. During an interview on a Robbie Shepherd radio programme, Robbie pondered who might be the person behind the scenes at Stronach responsible for telling all these tales. "Is it Buff Hardie?" he wondered, which we took as a great compliment. "Is it the lady who writes Stouriebog?" (a weekly diary of a farmer's wife, also in the Press and Journal).

Faced with this incisive questioning, I let the secret go. The response was . . . well . . . next to nothing. Revealing the secret we had guarded jealously for five years made no difference whatsoever. We still had the letters arriving at the Press and Journal asking after the villagers; offering Gibby Spurtle gardening tips, and correcting Babbie or Virginia on some home-baking procedural matter or other. In some ways, it was rather disappointing to think of all that wasted effort in security. But the more we thought about it, the more pleased we were, for it showed us that readers were quite comfortable with the Stronach they had come to know, thank you very much, and were unconcerned with whatever writer was filing his reports from the village. That is entirely as it should be.

Just as a by-the-way, that is also why we decided early in Stronach's career that we would never publish a map of the village, despite innumerable requests to do so. When enthusiasts wrote in asking for a map, we had to explain, rather shamefacedly, that the Ordnance Survey cartographers had mislaid their drawings after Erchie Sotter swicked them into a long session down at the Stronach Arms and promptly purloined their plans for puckish purposes. The requests for maps have diminished now, which I hope means that readers have gradually come to grips in their mind's eye with how the Emporium relates to Babbie Girn's house; how Meggie Bachle's croft looks as it sits up on the Hill of Stronach, and how long it takes Gibby Spurtle to walk from his house to the potting shed at Crochlie Neuk Eventide Home every morning to start work.

Which brings me to the second question that I mentioned away back at the start of this foreword: Where do you get your ideas?

There are dangers in answering this honestly. If I say that an upbringing in a small Aberdeenshire village provides a writer with a wealth of genuine background Stronach material, I lay myself open to about 15 different lawsuits. Let's just say that an awful lot of the character traits are traits I used to observe as a small boy. Sadly, these are increasingly less common as, one by one, all the old worthies pass on and are replaced by others who, shall we say, are less familiar with the ways of the North-east.

Anyone who grew up on a farm, or in a village or small town will know what I mean about characters and worthies, for every community remembers these individuals and the modern legends and tall tales which circulate about them. In many ways, these are the people responsible for the birth of Stronach. Often, all it takes to spark a story is a passing thought about someone I knew and how they might have expressed an opinion about some bizarre item in the news. Babbie, Virginia, Ebenezer and Co take over and I let them get on with it.

"Do you never run out of ideas?" is another popular question.

The answer is: "No."

With 15 principal characters bickering, shouting and clamouring to appear in any story, the problem is often deciding what (and who) to leave out. Often, I will be in the least expected places when a character drifts into my head saying something or another and I have to rush to find a pen and paper before the notion evaporates. *(This boy's a nutter — G. Spurtle)*.

More than once I have stopped the car, rushed into a newsagent for a pad and a pencil and gone back to sit behind the wheel outside sketching out a storyline. One of the most successful episodes (it appears in this book, but I'm not telling which one) was roughed out and written in the departures lounge of Charles DeGaulle Airport, Paris, while waiting several hours for a delayed connection and finding myself seated next to a group of Americans preparing to fly home to Philadelphia after "finding their roots".

Stronach episodes have been written all over the USA, Europe, the British Isles and twice, memorably, beyond the Arctic Circle in the old Soviet Union. I have often wondered what hotel fax operators made of the Doric as they sent back all those "fits", "fas" and "faes" to Aberdeen, Scotland.

Is it not difficult to write Doric dialogue when you're in foreign climes surrounded by foreign speech rhythms? On the contrary, the dialect comes through with even greater crystal clarity the farther from home you go. I now understand why exiles abroad are more Scottish than we Scots at home. It's not because they are maudlin or pining; it is simply because it is so much easier.

Besides, everywhere I go Babbie and Aggie and Walter and Geneva and all the others follow me. I confessed once on radio to hearing their voices as each story finally gelled and then just sitting down at the keyboard and letting them speak. It sounded daft at the time, I knew, and it probably sounds even more daft now, but nevertheless it is true. Once Babbie or Erchie or Dorothy is fired up to say something, I just sit down at the keyboard and let them say it. The words flow easily enough. *(This boy's definitely a nutter — G. Spurtle)*

Who is the favourite character? Well, that would be telling. I can say that Mother Dreep and Babbie Girn run neck and neck in the reader-popularity stakes. The North and North-east seem to be just as matriarchal now as they always have been, and probably always will be. Good, strong, opinionated women always seem to take a trick. *(Jist get on wi't — B. Girn)*

So there you have it, a potted insight into the world of Stronach. I hope it hasn't put you off these homely folk from a homely village in a most welcoming part of Scotland. *(Pass me a bucket — K. Barrington-Graham)*

And *if* I can get past all these interruptions from people who really ought to know better *(Are you sayin we canna behave wirsels in company? — E. Grip)*, I'll simply bid you welcome to this third annual special outing of Stronach; wish you a pleasant stay among us, and hope that you enjoy your book.

*(Ken this, I thocht he'd nivver stop. What a lay-aff aboot nithing ata. — D. Birze)*

NORMAN HARPER
Stronach
November, 1994


*(Mine's a double — E. Sotter)*

9

# Stronach

## Sheila Sunshine, of the Radio North-east holiday programme Days Here and There, spends a few hours in a typical Scots village

GOOD Morning. In today's programme, we ask if the only surefire way to get a seat on a British train is to become a train-driver. We ask why second honeymoons in the Caribbean are becoming so popular. Will you really feel like a new man after one? More important, will your wife? And we look at the case of the pensioner from Turriff who went on holiday to Australia where he swallowed a boomerang and was admitted to hospital 98 times.

But first, a growing trend in the travel market is the stay-at-home holiday. For whatever reason, more Scots are opting to stay in their native land to enjoy the rolling splendour of the hills, the purple majesty of the heather and the extortionate pricing of the tourist destinations.

The village of Stronach, tucked away in an upland corner of the North-east, is one of those deceptive little places in the back of beyond, where nothing seems to happen and where there are next to no amenties, but where, due largely to the bonhomie and warmth of the people, tourists can while away several peaceful days and really feel as if they have had a break.

We spent a couple of days there recently experiencing the best that Stronach has to offer. You will all have heard the saying that Scotland can offer everything a foreign destination can — except the weather. While we were there, it rained only twice — 19 hours in the first day and 22 in the second.

It is important to get your bearings quickly when you have only a short time in a new location, and how better to achieve that than by enlisting the aid of a willing resident? Our unofficial guide and mentor, Mr Erchie Sotter, took us under his wing. On a leisurely stroll round the village, we began discussing the relative merits of Stronach, compared to the more traditional European destinations, as a potential holiday spot.

"Mr Sotter, what can Stronach offer the stay-at-home tourist?"

"Weel, lass, Stronach's got a'thing, really. Ye can go walkin. Ye can go shoppin. Ye can go for a stroll roon the village. I recommend the stroll because ye can tak a teetie in folk's windaes — that's aye an entertainment and it's free. Ye widna believe the number o' tourists walkin up and doon the street gawpin and starin at folk in their ain front rooms. Mony's the time I've been standin there wi a mugga tea in ma haun and ma semmit on, wavin til holidaymakers oot on the street. Well, ye maun be an ambassador for yer village, I aye think. Widn't ye say? Of coorse, Stronach's got landmarks, as weel. Tak a looka my hearin-aid. Go on, tak a look. Dinna be feart. Bore in aboot. That's the stuff. Hae a richt look. Fit think ye? That's the latest model, that. The micro-technology that built my hearin-aid wis developed for America's space programme. Helluva dear, bit I got it on the National Health. It's revolutionised my hale life.

"Now I bet ye didna ken that the man that invented this latest micro-processor hearin-aid, in use in the American space programme, his a holiday home at Stronach?"

"No, we didn't? What's his name?"

"It's aboot half past ten."

"I see. Eh . . . are there any other notables in the village?"

"Well, twa doors doon fae the post office there's the woman wi the biggest femly in the North of Scotland. Her and her husband hiv hid fifteen kids and she still keeps cheery. Their ages rin fae fifteen doon til the baby she hid fower wikks ago."

"My goodness, but that's one a year. How on earth does she cope with so many young ones to look after? What does her husband do?"

"Oh, her husband's left her."

"Left her? You mean her husband's gone for good? How could he be so callous as to leave a poor woman struggling with 15 children on her own? How long ago did he leave her?"

"Thirteen year ago."

"Thirteen years? I thought you said she and her husband had had one baby a year right up until this year?"

"He kept comin back ti say he wis sorry."

"I see. Tell me, Mr Sotter, you're obviously very keen on the merits of your home patch, but have you ever been abroad? I mean have you ..."

"Lassie, lassie, lassie. Ye're lookin at one o' the maist decoratit sojers fae World War Two. I wis a Desert Rat, me. Focht Jerry in Singapore, Normandy, Anzio, Arnhem and onywye far I thocht I could crack lugs good and hard. Ye see, I wis ..."

"No, I mean more as a tourist visiting foreign climes. Have you been on holiday abroad? Does anything abroad compare with Stronach?"

"Well, nae really. I tried a sightseein holiday in Switzerland wi ma son and dother-in-law ae year, bit I couldna see onything for hills."

"I see. Anywhere else?"

"I went til Majorca three-fower year ago and the weather wis terrible. Absolutely terrible. Not a dry day the hale fortnicht. What broon I wis fin I come back."

"I thought you said it was raining all the time."

"Nae sunburn. Roost."

"I see. Mr Sotter, what about local pastimes at Stronach? There has to be more to do here than just walking up and down the street all day and looking into people's windows."

"Well, there's the angling."

"Ah, angling. Now that *is* interesting. And it's a very lucrative business.

11

Very good for the local economy. It pumps an awful lot of cash into hundreds of small communities like Stronach. Tell me, is the angling round about here good? Is it expensive?"

"It's nae expensive if ye're wi me, lass. As lang as ye're fleet on yer feet, it winna cost ye a penny."

"I see. And the river — the Water of Bogensharn — is it a good river for fish?"

"Exceptional. Aye, it's an exceptional river for the fish. It must be, for they dinna like leavin it."

"I see. Well, thank you very much, Mr Erchie Sotter."

"Is that us finished already? Surely no? I hinna telt ye aboot the Stronach Arms yet, hiv I?"

"No you haven't. Maybe that's a subject for some future programme."

"Bit the Stronach Arms is a real homely pubbie. Ye'd get a richt flavour o' village hospitality. In fact, there's a few flavours we could get there. I could tak ye there richt this minute."

"Thank you, Mr Sotter, but we'll have to be moving along."

"It's nae trouble, really."

"No, no, honestly, you've been very helpful."

"I could be a lot mair helpful. John the Barman's a good palla mine."

"I'm pleased for you, but I must be moving on."

"It's on yer road . . ."

"Thank you, listeners. And we'll be back again next week with another location report from a holiday spot somewhere in the British Isles."

"They dee rare stovies and a' thing . . ."

"Mr Sotter, *please.*"

"Oatcakes and a cuppie o' milk thrown in . . ."

# My Secret Stronach

Vale residents
share their little
hidden places

# Meggie Bachle

    "I canna really say that I've got a secret place. I've only got the one place — this little hoosie up at the top o' the hill, and there's nae muckle secret aboot it. We hinna ony locks on the doors, ye see. I've nivver seen the need really. It's nae as if we've onything worth pinchin. Claude got real modest at the hinder end o' last year and said he thocht it wid maybe be a good idea if we got a lock on the lavvie door oot in the close, bit I jist said: 'Dash it, Claude,' I said, 'I've been here mair nor fifty year and there's naeb'dy pinched a bucketfae yet.'

The ither rare thing aboot bidin up here is that ye're nae pestered wi naeb'dy. I've sometimes been doon in the village wi a load o' eggs for Mr Grip at the Emporium and as I'm bikin back throwe the village on ma road hame I can look in the windaes and I see folk newsin awa roon aboot their firesides and I thinks til masel: 'Meggie,' I thinks, 'ye're better aff far ye are. Nae botherin naeb'dy and naeb'dy botherin ye.' Aye, ye fair get yer privacy up here.

I worry aboot Claude, though. He's a good loon, bit he's nae affa clivver. I can say that because I'm his mither, though I widna thole it fae a stranger. I often winder if a life awa up here wi jist me for company is really good for a young laddie. Especially in the winter. What affa winters we get up here. Cuts richt through a body lik a spad through sharn.

We'd an affa winter last year, for instance. Ae mornin, I says til Claude, I says: 'Claude,' I says, 'It's surely freezin caul ootside this mornin,' I says. So he wanders across til the windae and he says: 'I couldna richt say. A'thing's covered in sna.'

Anither good thing aboot bidin oot here is that ye're nae bothered wi salesmen. I canna be deein wi folk that bowl up at yer door needin ye ti buy stuff. I usually sell them a dizzen eggs and then they leave.

I'd a boy at the door twa year syne hopin I wid buy encyclopedias. I ask ye. Encyclopedias? Me? 'Awa ye go,' I says, 'I'm nae sikkin yer encyclopedias.' Then he looks at Claude and he says: 'But your boy's education is at stake. Are you sure that his education is up to scratch? Could he not be doing with a little help to get himself ahead of his classmates? You would be investing in his future and in your own old age, madam.' An affa lay-aff he hid. Then he turns til Claude. 'Tell me, young man,' he says, 'can you tell me what family the crocodile belongs to?'

Claude looks at him and I could see he wis thinkin hard— peer loon— and he says: 'Well, I'm sorry, mister,' he says, "bit I didna ken there wis onybody hereaboots kept a crocodile.'

Then a twa-three wikks syne we'd this young lad stopped in the fairm close wi his van, and I'm lookin oot the scullery windae and I sees him unloadin this great big hoover. He knocks on the back door and I opens it and he says: 'What a lovely house, but I can show you how it could be even lovelier. I can show you how technology will make light of all your housework.' And he barges past me and ben intil the sittin-room. What a rate he wis at. I couldna stop him.

Then he stands up in the sittin-room and he says: 'Madam, this is the vacuum-cleaner of your dreams. This is the vacuum-cleaner you have been waiting for all your life.' I telt him I wisna sikkin a vacuum-cleaner. Bit wid he listen?

He says: 'Madam, I challenge you to a £50 wager.' And then he teemed this great big bagga soot a' ower ma sittin-room lino. Soot a'wye, there wis. Ma hale front room wis black as the Ace o' Picks. What a soss.

'Madam,' he says, 'if this marvellous new vacuum-cleaner, with the latest Scandinavian cleaning technology cannot get your flooring clean of all this soot, and make it even cleaner than it was before, I am authorised to pay you not £10, not £20, but £50, madam. Yes, indeed, you will receive this crisp £50 note into your hand if you agree to the trial and if my cleaner is defeated.'

Well, I jist lookit at him. He stood in the soot and he worked his heels hard in. I suppose he wis needin a richt mess.

Then he lookit up at me and he smiled, and he said: 'So, madam,' he says, 'are you game to take me on? Are you prepared to challenge the combined industrial might of one of the largest companies in Europe and the ingenuity of the 21st century?'

I says: 'Fairly that, laddie. We hinna ony electric in this hoose.'

MARGARET BACHLE (52)
**lives the most meagre existence in the Howe of Stronach — with her teenage son, Claude, in a tumbledown croft at the top of the Hill of Stronach.**
**They have little visible means of support, but Miss Bachle sells eggs to Ebenezer Grip at the Stronach Emporium and General Stores once a week and seems to earn enough to scrape by.**
**She is conscious, however, that a teenage son needs a good deal of looking after, and that such care is not cheap.**
**She is currently engaged in researching new commercial avenues vis-a-vis eggs, but so far has not come up with anything notably new.**
**There is no truth in the scurrilous rumour currently doing the rounds that she is feeding her hens whisky in the hope that they will produce Scotch Eggs.**

15

# Kate Barrington-Graham

66 I cannot say that I have any particularly secret places in or near the village. I find it is so important to be seen, and it would rather defeat the object of the exercise to be skulking about in secret, don't you think?"

A high profile is of immense importance when one is a community icon, as I am. I ask you, have ever you heard of someone in authority shying away from public attention; from the gaze of the crowds? Exactly. And that is why I cannot deny myself to the people of the village. They need to know that someone of standing is there.

A vital element in this is entertaining. I wouldn't claim to entertain the masses at Bridge House, but we do find time to squeeze in a few close chums, you know. We have provosts and councillors and headmasters and sheriffs and bankers and clergymen at our table very regularly. It oils the social wheels.

For instance, in my role as chairperson of Stronach Community Council, I know that sometimes we can find ourselves up against a particularly protracted problem. All I have to do is dial one of our dinner guests and I simply know that the problem will be sorted out within minutes. That's all there is to it. You see what I mean about contacts having benefits far beyond the dinner table?

Contacts are useful provided you are prepared to work at them, of course. You can't just invite someone round for post-Haddo canapés, then ignore them for years and expect them to deliver the goods when required. You have to cultivate and maintain your social network.

How does one begin? I knew you would ask. You begin, that's all. You just do it. Everyone has to start somewhere. I started small, when I was a young mother back in Oxfordshire. Godfrey was still working for a multinational conglomerate at that stage; he hadn't set up his own consultancy. That was still off in a glittering future. And I knew very quickly that it was vital to be seen and to be seen to be accommodating, too. So despite the trials of bringing up two lively and active young children, Octavia and Piers, I surrendered myself willingly to the hurly-burly of the social circuit. Life's such a trial.

It soon paid dividends. I think there is a direct correlation between the frequency of entertaining a divisional director and the speed with which your spouse accelerates up the promotional ladder. I make no bones about it. We had the divisional director to tea at least once every couple of months. Within a year, Godfrey was his deputy. Don't tell me that my salmon pancakes didn't have a lot to do with that.

Of course, entertaining the professions is important, but one might as well be invisble if one does not entertain socially within the community, too. We calculated very quickly that a vital dinner guest to get on the fast track for social acceptibility would be the Bishop. You can imagine what a trial that was to be. Nevertheless, I am not one to shirk a challenge, so I plunged in with both feet, picking up the protocol as I went along.

I read all the books I could find about forms of address, suitable topics of conversation and the etiquette of hosting such a senior clergyman. Research is so important, I find. Don't you?

I won't deny that it was my most challenging piece of hostessery. In fact, there were times when I questioned the wisdom of such vaulting ambition, but I put such a lot of work into it and I simply knew it would be a tremendous success. Piers and Octavia were quite worried about me, for they kept well clear. I think they could see I was agitated, the little poppets.

The bishop arrived — an imposing man, but not unbefitting so exalted an office — and Maid took his coat and bade him welcome.

We had a few sweet sherries and just as we were about to go into dinner, a little head appeared round the door. It was Octavia, in her little nightdress. I was aghast. I had schooled the children to be on best behaviour and not to venture downstairs once our guest had arrived.

I told her rather sharply to go back upstairs to bed, but the bishop would have none of it.

"Now, now, my child," he said, seating Octavia on his knee. "Never mind. You shall say grace for us."

Octavia was only six. She smiled an embarrassed little smile and looked at her daddy. "What is grace, daddy?" she asked.

"You know," said Godfrey, "what mummy said before lunch today."

So she clasped her little hands together, closed her eyes and said: "Oh God, why did I invite that damned man to dinner?"

**MRS KATHARINE AMANDA VICTORIA BARRINGTON-GRAHAM (49)**
is a comparatively recent arrival in the Howe of Stronach, moving north from her native Cotswolds in 1985 with business-consultant husband, Godfrey. However, her inexperience has not prevented her from playing a full part in the life of Stronach.

As well as being president of the WRI, she is chairperson of the community council, the PTA, the Stronach Amenities Committee, the Pensioners' Club, the Village Hall Trust, the Park Committee, the Drama Club, the Kirk Guild and several other associations which she feels the local people couldn't quite manage to the same degree.

The Barrington-Grahams are socially a little more formal than others in the village. They are said to wear evening dress in their sauna.

# Dorothy Birze

❝My favourite place in Stronach is ony place except in ma hoose. That maybe sounds funny, except if ye're aul and lonely like me. The days are affa lang fan ye bide yersel. If you bide yersel, ye'll ken fit I mean. The postie wid be ma lifeline, and I used ti sit at the windae waitin for him, bit I stopped that. I dinna look for him noo. He passed by the gate maist days and it got affa disappintin. On the days he did come up the pathie, it wis usually some raffle fae the Reader's Digest.

I'm nae wallowin in self-pity or nithing. I've hid my young day and it's ither folk's turn noo. I jist wish that some young folk wid maybe gie me a wave fae the ither side o' the street or maybe jist smile in my direction. I go oot intil the gairden for as lang as I can stand, even in winter. That wye, ye get a Hello fae folk walkin up the street. I've noticed them crossin the road afore they get til me noo.

Nivver mind, I've got good news for ye. I've got twa lodgers. I've been needin company for a while and then I saw an advert in ma Press and Journal and I thocht it wid jist suit me richt.

*"Two male parrots for sale. Not talkers, but very well-behaved."*

And it gave a phone number in Aiberdeen. I couldna believe ma luck. I've aye liked parrots, ye see. Fan I wis a scullery maid at one o' the big hooses at Ellon atween the wars, they hid a parrot. I took a richt shine til him. A great big parrot, he wis. And what bonnie colours. Reid and yalla and blue and green. Nivver spoke, that wis the only thing.

Fan the boss wisna lookin, I wid nip intil the front room and try and get the parrot spikkin, bit nae success. I canna say I blamed the parrot. The boss hid an affa temper, and if he thocht the parrot wisna co-operatin he wid start shoutin and sweirin at it. Great bawlin and roarin performances he wid pit up wi this parrot and the parrot wid jist sit there on its perch, blinkin and pickin its beak. That jist annoyed the boss mair. I ask ye, if you wis a parrot bein treatit lik that, wid you co-operate? Certainly not.

Onywye, this particular mornin I wis helpin oot the upstairs maid wi the dustin fan the boss come back unexpected like. He strode intil the front room and he saw me wi ma duster and wax.

He strode across til the cage and the parrot jist sat there blinkin. "Well, you damned stupid bird," said the boss, "I've kept you in food and water and warmth for more than two years now and not a murmur out of you. You're a damned ungrateful wretch, that's what you are! WHAT ARE YOU! YOU'RE A DAMNED UNGRATEFUL WRETCH! CAN YOU TALK? CAN YOU TALK? EH? CAN YOU TALK AT ALL? OR ARE YOU JUST A DUMB CLUCK? YOU STUPID-LOOKING OBJECT! YOU STUPID CREATURE! CAN YOU TALK?"

Lord did the parrot nae squawk and say: "I can spik. Can you flee?"

I've admired parrots ivver since then, so this advert in the Press and Journal wis a Godsend for me. I went til the phone box and phoned the blokie and it turned oot he wis a Catholic priest and he'd been promotit and he didna hae the same time for lookin efter them and he wis needin a good home for them.

I went in on the bussie. He'd learned the parrots a trick. The twa o' them sat on their perches fiddlin wi rosary beads and, fan they spoke, they spoke in Latin prayers. I couldna hardly believe fit I wis seein and hearin. What bonnie birdies they were.

"I wid fairly gie them a good home, sir," I says, "bit I hinna much money." Well, the priest looked at me and he smiled and he said: "You're a good woman. I can tell. Here you go. I know you'll take good care of them. They're yours. And here's £20 to help with your costs."

I couldna believe ma luck. I got them hame and I wis that excitit. I thocht I wid spend the twenty poun gettin them some female company. Well, they lookit affa lonely sittin there wi their beads. So I bocht a budgie. A little lady budgie. And I took her hame.

The twa parrots were still in the cage, jist sittin there twiddlin their beads and mummlin their prayers. Then I opened the cage door and they looked up and they saw the budgie.

"Throw awa yer beads, Percy," says one. "That's wir prayers answered at last."

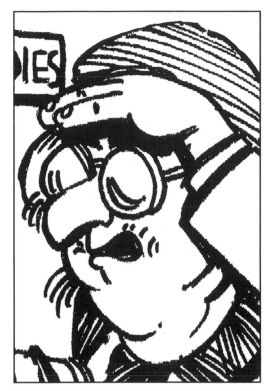

DOROTHY MIMA BIRZE **(62)**
**is one of the lonelier souls in the village. Her son, now living in London, pays her no attention.**

**As a result of her isolation, and the fact that she is relatively new in the village, Dorothy's closest companion was her budgie, Jocky. The relationship was fruitful and flourished.**

**Dorothy is not well off, but she saved enough from her pension to have a new living-room carpet fitted.**

**At the end of the job, the fitters noticed a bump in the middle of the room. Rather than go to the bother of lifting the carpet to smooth it out, they jumped on top of the bump several times until the carpet was flat.**

**Dorothy returned from the shops and said she hoped the fitters hadn't minded that she had let Jocky out of his cage for a breath of fresh air.**

# Geneva Brose

❝ I canna really pick a favourite secret place at Stronach because there's nae really ony secret places. The village is ower sma for secrets. I jist like the hale place. I widna change a single thing aboot it. Well, that's nae really true. I wid maybe change the folk that are grippy wi their money. Ye can sniff them a mile aff. Claes smellin o' mothballs. Ilky penny a prisoner. I've nae time for it.

Now, jist because I like Stronach disna mean I dinna like a change o' scene noo and again. I'm nae stuck in a rut. Sandy disna really go that much for holidays, so I usually rely on the Supporter's Club bus outins or the annual Stronach Picnic. I like the different scenery and gettin an oor or twa shoppin in a different toon or village. Well, it's a change o' loaf, isn't it?

I think the shops in Tayside are fairly the friendliest. Say fit ye like, bit the assistants in Dundee and Arbroath and Forfar and Brechin and Montrose and Blairgowrie and places lik that are jist the bee's knees as far as I'm concerned. Canna dee enough for ye.

They're cheaper, as weel. Ye can dee yer messages for a good ten poun cheaper in Dundee than ye can manage in Aiberdeen, I'm nae carin fit onybody says. What a price things are in Aiberdeen nooadays. I likes ma food fresh, bit my goodness ye pey through the nose for it in The Toon.

I passed a rare window display o' fruit and bakery and stuff like that on Setterday, so I thocht: "There's somebody that taks a pride in their shop, so I'll encourage them wi ma trade."

I went in and there's this snooty young laddie that looked like he'd a bad smell under his nose. He must hiv been the owner's son.

I says: "I'll tak a halfie o' chopped pork," I says.

"I'm sorry, madam," he says, snooty-like, "but we sell by the kilogram. I'm afraid our usual clientele tend not to deal in minimal purchasing."

"Oh," I says, "well, I'll tak a kilogram of your chappit pork than. It'll mak rare sandwiches and we can hae it for wir supper a' this wikk. Fit like cheese hiv ye got?"

"Madam," he says, "we have Norwegian Jarlsberg freshly imported this morning, and we have a new Russian sheep's cheese which is proving extremely popular with our account customers in Rubislaw Den."

"So ye hinna Dairylea Spread?" I says. He didna even bother replyin.

"I'll tak a half-dizzen o' yer Grunny Smiths," I said.

"Madam," he says. "those are not Granny Smiths. Those are Javan Morning Glory, flown in fresh from the East Indies only yesterday."

"Oh, well," I says. "Gie's a half-dizzen o' yer Morning Glories. Hiv ye ony coffee?"

"Instant, ground or beans?" he says.

"Well," I says, "I'm hopin ye've got instant."

"Of course, madam," he says, "we have a freeze-dried Venezuelan blend hand-picked by the young women of the hill slopes, shipped the same day to a respected coffee house in Paris where some of the most experienced coffee noses in Europe carefully select the coffees, bean by bean, to make up the most prized blended beverage in Paris at the moment."

"I see," I says. "So I suppose that means ye hinna ony Mellow Birds." He didna reply again.

"OK," I says, "gies a little jarrie o' yer Venusian freeze-dried."

"Certainly madam," he says. "will that be everything?"

"I think so," I says.

"All right," he says, "that's one kilogram of processed meat from the plains of Patagonia, six prime specimens of Javan Morning Glory Apples and a 250-gramme jar of Parisian Palate coffee. Let me see, now. Let me see. Yes, that will be fifteen pounds ninety-seven pence altogether."

"Fit?" I says. "Fifteen ninety-sivven? Ye're jokin. Fifteen ninety-sivven? For that? Ye can stick that for a game o' sojers, laddie. That's daylight robbery. I'm nae peyin sixteen quid for that. Nae even Ebenezer Grip charges that and he can charge like the Light Brigade.

And I stormed oot. Jist afore I reached the door, I turned and went back and slappit fifty pee doon on the coonter.

"What is that madam?" he said, snootier than ivver.

"That's fifty pee, sonny," I said. "You keep it. I stood on a grape on ma road oot."

**GENEVA FLORETTA VIENNA BROSE finds that her greatest trial in life is her husband, Sandy. Despite almost 40 years of marriage, she daydreams every so often about what might have been had she married the man of her dreams, American 1950s actor Montgomery Clift.**

**As she gazes at Sandy snoring in the easy chair by the fireside, Press and Journal fluttering over his face with each booming breath, she wonders if life has not passed her by.**

**She realises that she cannot complain too much, for Sandy is always keen to take her on an evening out, and not every wife can say that, although she wishes he was not quite such an embarrassment in company.**

**At dinner-dances, towards the end of the evening, Sandy frequently leans across to her and warns her to drink no more as her face is getting blurry.**

# Sandy Brose

**" "** Quite frankly, my favourite place is ma ain fireside. It's guaranteed peace and quaet in my comfy easy cheir. A man needs a place lik that, especially if he's a mairriet man. Am I richt, lads? Ye need an oasis in a stormy sea o' hooverin, dustin and settin the table.

I canna say my Geneva's a bad sort. She nags me noo and again, bit basically she understands that a man's a man and that she can rely on me for onything, especially if it's tips for the horses or nippin doon til the shoppie for fower cans o' export. Women need reassurin that ye're reliable that wye. Am I richt, lads?

I dinna agree wi men that misca' their wives in public. That's nae affa polite, that, is it? If ye must misca' them, misca' them til their face, that's my motto. Mind and pit the coalpail on yer heid first.

I wis at a denner-dunce wi Geneva a few wikkends ago. We often tak a tekkie oot and aboot. We likes a change noo and again. We endit up at a table wi this couple fae Bumff. Nice couple. Bit efter he'd a coupla drinks he began gettin affa loud. His wife wis real embarrassed. "Jimmy," she says, "come doon aff the table wi that microphone and stop singin." Bit he nivver looked the road o' her.

Onywye, we got him doon aff the table and he floppit back intil his seat and his tie wis squint and his jacket wis a' crumpled and his een wis half-shut and we thocht we'd heard the last o' him. Lord, did he nae sit up again and start shoutin at his wife. I says til the blokie, I says: "Dinna be nesty til yer wife," I says.

"I'm nae nesty til ma wife," he says, "I love ma wife. She's ma darlin angel. She's ma little tulip. She's ma lovie-dovie." Some affa rubbish he wis comin oot wi. Then he says: "In fact, she's ma peach." Then he began slubberin in aboot til her wi great big noisy kisses.

I says: "Well, that's good, that," I says. "Yer wife's yer peach. Is that because she's saft, sweet and juicy?"

"No," he says. "It's because she's got a hert o' stone."

That wisna affa nice, that, wis it? Am I richt, lads?

Of coorse, I'm nae sayin I hinna hid a rovin eye masel in ma time. There's life in the aul dog yet. I'm maybe retired, bit there's still a roarin fire in ma biler. The thing is, Geneva keeps me on sic a short rope that I couldna even think aboot that kinna thing, for she wid surely find oot. She's affa nosey that wye, Geneva.

I mind ae nicht ma bus broke doon in the middle o' winter. Naebody on it. Nae hooses for miles. And nae hope o' lettin Geneva ken fit wis adee. I wis jist sittin there workin oot a plan fan a young lassie stops in front o' ma bus in this little yalla sports car. "Can I help?" she says. A rare lookin lassie she wis. Slim and lang blonde hair and a little wee mini skirt wi the kinky beets and a' thing." I says: "Ma bussie's broken doon," I says. "And I canna report it."

"Not a problem," she says. "Come to my cottage and you can phone from there."

So I locks up the bussie and I loups intil her little sports car and we race aff til her hoose. Michty, did her hand nae start wanderin a' ower ma knees. I says til masel: "Michty, Sandy," I says.

We got in and she showed me her phone. Fan I wis phonin the mechanic, she wis in the kitchen. Then she produced this slap-up feed. Fan I wis eating the feed she appeared in the door weerin a wispy see-through negligy."

"I says: "Na, na," I says. "Sae far and nae farrer, Sandy, ma lad."

So she took me back til the bussie and I thankit her and I got goin again and I'm drivin intil Stronach and I'm thinkin if Geneva finds oot aboot this she'll go feel. She'll nivver believe me that nithing happened. Honesty is the best policy.

"And far hiv you been?" she says fan I got in ower the front door.

"Well, ma dear," I says, "ma bussie broke doon and this bonnie young lassie in a yalla sports car took me back til her place and her hands were a' ower me and she made me a meal and then she tried gettin aff wi me by weerin this little wispy see-through nightie."

She clappit ma lugs.

"Dinna you tell me ony mair o' yer dampt lees, Sandy Brose," she says. "Ye've been doon at that dampt pub playin dominoes."

**ALEXANDER CLARENCE BROSE (64) is not noted for physical activity, which explains his ample girth and somnolent nature since he retired from his job as a bus driver on the Stronach-Aberdeen-Stronach route.**

**Mr Brose is one of life's easier-natured characters; a creature of habit, who likes his Thursday-evening pint at the Stronach Arms, a wee flutter on the horses and a snooze in his armchair.**

**Mr Brose has a kind heart, however. When looking for a silver-wedding gift for his wife, Geneva, he selected a clutch cable for a 1982 Ford Escort 1.3GL.**

**The assistant at the garage asked if he would like it wrapped so that it would be a surprise.**

**"Aye," he said. "Wrap it. That wye, it'll be a double surprise; she's expectin a silver bracelet."**

# Aggie Dreep

"There's only one favourite place for me at Stronach and that's the stage at the village hall durin the prizegivin at the industrial show.

The feelin ye get fan ye're up there wi yer Madeira cake, yer rasp jam and yer bannocks a' roon aboot ye — I jist canna describe it. The fact that it's usually me wi the prizes and nae Geneva Brose, well, that's jist the icin on the cake, isn't it?

Yes, Geneva and me's still argy-bargyin. It winna get ony better noo. We startit rowin at the school. We were rowin durin wir coortin days. And we've been rowin ivver since. We're ower aul for peace treaties. Nae neen o' yer Northern Ireland here. John Hume wid get short shrift at Stronach.

The thing is, I'm nae really an aggressive person. I'm nae. A'body thinks I'm an aul battleaxe wi a temper, bit I'm nae. Really, I'm nae. Jist ask my Walter. *(Aye, she is — W.D.)*

Bit I jist need a glimpse o' that wifie Brose and I can feel ma knivs tichtenin and ma teeth scrapin and I jist feel lik hittin her. Isn't that affa? I ken she's an objectionable wifie and Mother Teresa wid kick her shins, bit ye shouldna be feelin that wye aboot somebody.

Things came til a heid at the industrial show in August. She wis smirkin at ma doughrings. That kinna half-leer that ye see on Penelope Keith noo and again. And I jist couldna control masel. I jist marched ower, picked up a gless o' Gibby Spurtle's rhubarb wine and flung it at her. The hale place went silent. I couldna believe fit I did. I dinna think onybody else could, eether.

I wis really embarrassed, of coorse. Walter wis embarrassed as weel. At hame that nicht he said he couldna understand fit hid come ower mne, and I jist broke doon sobbin. He said he thocht I needit help.

"Fit kinna help?" I said.

"Well, he said, "the doctor first, bit I think ye maybe need an oor or twa wi a psychiatrist. Yer behaviour's nae normal."

"Nae a psychiatrist," I said. "Not on yer nellie."

"There's nae shame in seein a shrink nooadays," he said. "I believe they can be really helpful and naebody wid ken."

I didna agree or disagree. I said I wid sleep on it. Bit I didna get ony sleep ata that nicht. I jist lay there, gazin at the ceilin and thinkin aboot masel and how embarrassed I'd been and how embarrassin it must hiv been for Walter.

At breakfast the next mornin, I said I wid go and see the doctor that nicht, although I thocht I wis feelin a bittie better.

I spoke too soon. I walked intil the pensioners' lunch club in the village hall and there wis Geneva dishin oot the sprouts, and I jist heard her sayin: "Ye widna get sprouts like that fae the wifie Dreep. Hers are lik bullets."

24

I jist lost ma rag again. I took a gless o' orange cordial fae Fobbie Pluffer's hand and I flung it at the wifie Brose and turned and stormed oot. I think that wis the moment I kent I needit help. Things wis jist gettin ower embarrassin. I couldna go on at a hicht lik that.

So I signed up with the psychiatrist. An affa nice blokie. Really soft-spoken and understandin. And I jist let it a' pour oot. Richt back til ma schooldays, and then ma coortin days, and ma weddin, and the WRI and the wifie Brose and a'thing.

He nivver offered an opinion, I noticed. He jist listened. Bit I canna tell ye how helpful that wis. He showed me that it wis an inferiority complex that wis makkin me behave in an embarrassin manner. He said that embarrassment wis a natural reaction and that anger wis a natural reaction and that the trick wis controllin the two.

So, jist last wikk I wis helpin oot at the young mums and toddlers club at the village hall and there wis Geneva again. I thocht maybe the time hid come for peace. Then, jist as I wis approachin her wi ma hand stretched oot, I heard her sayin til a baby:

"There ye go, baby. Yer saps is jist lik Aggie Dreep's cookin. Tasteless."

I took up a gless o' watter and I flung it at her and walked oot.

"Ye've deen it again!" she shouted.

"I ken," I said. "Bit at least it disna embarrass me noo."

AGNES CATHERINE SUSAN DREEP (53) makes a formdable figure in the village. It is a brave man or woman who crosses Aggie, but at least the object of most of her ire and derision is only one person — Geneva Brose. The feud between them began when both attended Stronach Primary School and has been maintained at full tilt to the present day. Only once has it seemed likely to subside — when both gave birth in 1968. Mrs Dreep stopped Mrs Brose and pram in the street and made a great fuss of Mrs Brose's new baby daughter, expecting Mrs Brose to return the compliment. Mrs Brose did not. Consequently, Mrs Dreep looked into the pram again. "She's affa like her faither," she pronounced. "Div ye think so?" said Mrs Brose. "Oh, definitely," said Mrs Dreep. "Lyin on her back clutchin a bottle."

# Mother Dreep

❝Dinna bother me wi yer secret places. A lotta dampt nonsense. In my young day we'd nae time for secret places. We were ower busy workin.

Fairms were like that during the first war. Up at five ilky mornin and work, work, work. Nae in wir beds til nine or ten at nicht and nivver a minute til wirsels. The young folk nooadays is saft. Saft in the belly and saft in the heid. They couldna manage the work we managed. We were hardy in my young day, and prood o' wirsels. The kids nooadays hiv nae self-respeck. They moloch aboot here and they slouch aboot there, listenin til their gramophones and watchin their TV. They jist annoy me. So dinna you come here sikkin news o' secret places, because we hidna ony. Fairms wis nae places for secrets.

Yes, I came fae a fairm. I wis a kitchie-deem at ma faither's fairm at Memsie. Then I met Doddie and we set up at Wester Boggiedubs o' Stronach, and here I've been ivver since.

No, I'd nae trouble rinnin a cottar hoose. That wis ma trainin fae gey near fan I could walk. Quines wis brocht up for hoosework in that times, and we didna think onything o' it.

Aye, and nae jist hoosework. Mony's the time I wis socht for heavy labour roon aboot the fairm. Ye jist put yer back intil it and got on wi't. Nooadays, they'd be worried aboot brakkin their nails or some dampt stupidness.

It wis pigs that we kept. I widna say we won prizes, though we aye came awa fae the Stronach Show wi respectable results, as ye micht say. Doddie wis the expert on the pig-breedin. He wid roam a' ower the place in the horse and trap looking for pigs for breedin wi. Usually, we just put oor soos ower til the ither side o' the howe and the fairmer at Wester Bogensharn.

I mind in 1932 we'd three great big soos that we were needin matit, and Doddie got a shottie o' an aul vannie fae somebody at the garage in the village and he drove them ower.

The time the soos wis bein matit, Doddie wis workin oot a price wi Aul Bogies and he askit how he wid ken if the matin hid been a success.

"Well," says Aul Bogies, "you look oot at yer soos the morn's mornin. If they're eatin grass, it's a success. If they're rollin aboot amon dubs, it hisna."

So Doddie came hame and the next mornin he wis up in his semmit and lookin oot the windae at the pigs in the park below.

"Well?" I says.

"They're rollin aboot amon dubs," he said. "We'd better tak theam back ower til Aul Bogies."

So Doddie hauled on his brikks and he got the vannie oot fae the top barn far the garageman hid said we could keep it and he loadit up the three soos and ower he went til Aul Bogies again.

"I'm sorry, Bogies," he said, "bit I doot it didna tak the first time."

That's a' richt, Doddie," says Bogies. "We'd better pit them in aside Kitchener again." Kitchener wis the name o' the boar.

The next mornin, Doddie wis up at the cracka dawn again and lookin oot the windae.

"Na, na, na," he says. "Rollin aboot amon dubs again. That's anither mornin wastit by the time I get them ower til Aul Bogies again."

He wisna in an affa good humour, I can tell ye. Doddie wis like that if things didna go the wye they were supposed. He wis affa short on the fuse.

So he loads up the three soos in the Aul Vannie and off he sets again for the ither side o' the howe and Kitchener.

Back they come jist afore denner-time and he lets the three soos oot in the park aneth the hoose. "Well, I hope that's the last o' that," he says, "for I hinna the time for caperin aboot wi soos and Kitchener. There's a fairm here needin atten-tion."

I wis jist on tenterhooks a' nicht. I couldna get slept. I wis near feart at fit Doddie wid dee if the soos hidna been served richt this time. So afore he wis richt wakkened, I got oot o' the bed and I tiptoed across til the windae as quaet as a moosie.

He heard me, though. He wis an affa licht sleeper, Doddie. "Well?" he said. "Are they rollin aboot amon the dubs this mornin?"

"No," I says.

"Thank the Lord for that," he said.

"No," I said. "There's twa in the back o' the vannie and the ither een's inside peepin the horn."

ISABELLA SCATTERTY DREEP (94) is the oldest resident in the Howe of Stronach and so has the honour of being visited by the minister with a bunch of flowers from the Kirk Session every Christmas Eve. It is an honour she prizes.

Mother Dreep's great age entitles her to robust attitudes and firm opinions which she is not slow to share with others. She is the only person known to have bettered her daughter-in-law, Agnes, in argu-ment, and likes nothing better than Jehovah's Witnesses and political canvassers calling. Within 15 minutes they beat a hasty retreat.

Mother Dreep can claim a distin-guished lineage and has traced her ancestry back to 1742. She is proud to be able to claim that one of her forebears fell at Waterloo — pushed off Platform Six.

# Walter Dreep

66I KEN fine you folk think I'll say my favourite place at Stronach is in front o' the kitchen sink, or standin at a hot stove, or oot on the back green hingin oot the washin. I ken fine folk think I'm hen-pecked. I ken folk lach ahen ma back. I ken folk think I'm under Aggie's thoom. Well, jist so's ye understand, I'm nae in the least hen-pecked. Aggie agrees.

Aggie and I get on fine. We've wir ups and doons bit, on the whole, we weir awa. It's nae as if we're like her sister and brither-in-law. They're forever nae spikkin. He once telt me he hidna spoken til his wife in nearly 10 years. He said he couldna get a word in edgewyes.

The trick is, I think, that ye must let wives ken that they're cherished. They must understand that they mean the earth til ye. Pay them compliments. Flatter them. Tell them how nice they look, even if ye ken they look lik the back end o' a panto horse. Better still, pay them compliments in front o' ither folk. I aye pays Aggie a compliment if we're oot at the bingo.

Last wikkend, I said til the crowdie at wir bingo table. "Ye ken this, I've got the best wife in the Country."

A blokie at the table in ahen me turned roon and he says: "You're lucky. Mine bides wi me in The Toon."

Trust's affa important in a marriage, div ye nae think? I trust Aggie. She handles a' the financial side. I wis nivver affa good wi money. So I jist hands across my income til her and she looks efter it. They say that money is the main reason for marital discord. I *will* say that that probably applies wi Aggie and me. Once I hand ower the money, I hiv a devil o' a job gettin ony back.

I'm forever at her side askin for a twa-three poun for this or that. If I ask ower often, she snaps back at me. "Money, money, money," she says. "That's a' you're interestit in, Walter Dreep. Why are ye forever needin money? Fit div ye spend it on?"

"I dinna ken, dear," I tell her. "Ye nivver gie me ony."

I suppose ma favourite place in Stronach, deep-doon, is the barber's. I've been gettin ma hair cut there for as lang as I can mind. I hinna the same amount o' hair nooadays, of coorse, bit I still go back. He maks a show o' trimmin up a pucklie tufts roon aboot ma neck bit, really, I'm there for a news. Ye meet a' the worthies doon at the barber and ye can while awa an oor or twa crackin jokes and tellin stories. It sets ye up for yer ironin fan ye get hame.

I think the first time I went til that barber wis nae lang efter I wis demobbed. That wis roon aboot the time I wis coortin Aggie. She wis a gey fearsome lassie even then. I suppose I should hiv taen the hint, maybe, bit fan Cupid's arras hiv blindit ye, fit can ye dee?

They used ti joke aboot Aggie doon at the barber. They wid say things like: "Ye'll be a' richt wi Aggie, Wattie. She's got a rare sense o' rumour." Coorse stuff lik that.

I didna let it bother me, of course. If they see that it bothers ye they jist pile on the pressure even mair. Let it lie, Walter, I telt masel, and that's fit I did.

Then every so often that I went back til the barber, I wid notice he wis takkin an affa interest in Aggie. I thocht there wis something up. I thocht til masel: "Aye-aye, Wattie," I thocht. "here's something adee here. The barber's takkin an affa interest in your Aggie. Hiv ye got a rival in love?"

It wisna onything sinister, of course. Jist little snippets o' conversation. Bit he wis aye the one that brocht her up, and he seemed affa keen ti spik aboot her. Jist aboot ivry second sentence wis Aggie, Aggie, Aggie.

I wid sit doon in the cheir and he wid news awa for a minute or twa and then it wid start.

"And foo's Aggie the day?" he wid say, and I wid say that she wis deein fine, thank you very much.

Then he wid news about the weather or something, and then he wid say: "Aggie likes the sunshine, dis she?"

And I wid say: "Oh, aye; she fairly likes the sun, Aggie."

And then we wid news aboot the fitba, and he wid say: "Aggie disna go til Pittodrie wi ye?", and I wid turn in ma seat and I wid say: "Look, I'm sure there's nithing funny goin on, bit wid ye mind tellin me fit wye ye're affa interestit in Aggie?"

"I'm nae really," he said, "bit ivry time I mention her yer hair stands on end and it's an affa lot easier ti cut."

**WALTER ALOYSIUS DREEP (55) is a retired postman in the village and so is one of the best-kent faces in the vale. Another resident born and brought up at Stronach, he sees no reason to leave one of the bonniest spots in the North of Scotland.**

**Married to Aggie, he has not always known marital harmony, but feels he has managed to even up the odds by bringing his mother to stay with them in their front room. Now he is nagged on two fronts, which brings a certain balance to his life, he reports.**

**Mr Dreep is something of a philosopher and can often be seen walking along the streets of the village, plastic message-bag in hand, staring at the sky and daydreaming.**

**Of late, he has been considering his wedding, wondering why, if a bride wears white as a symbol of joy, does a groom always wear black?**

29

# Babbie Girn

““Ma favourite place is ma ain hoosie. At least, it wis until I wis burgled nine year ago. A burglary. At Stronach. I'd nivver hiv believed it. It leaves ye feelin chary, kennin that somebody else — some stranger — his been in yer hoose athoot yer permission, and that they've been through a' yer private things. Ye feel like a'thing needs a dampt good scrub, so I jist got oot the Jeyes Fluid and I did exactly that.

Ma neighbours rallied roon. I've got real good neighbours. Virginia on the one side and Erchie on the ither. Virginia helped me wi the cleanin oot, and Erchie helped me cleanin oot the sideboard far a' ma New Year drinks is kept.

I ken exactly fit the burglars wis fter. They wis efter the proceeds o' the sale o' my aul china tattie-pot — the pot that went up for auction and made me — well, that's my business how muckle it made me, bit it wis a tidy sum.

The thing is, I widna keep that kinna money in the hoose. That's a' doon at the bunk. I'm nae one o' these folk that keeps money in the po or in the tumble-drier or queer places like that.

For ae thing, I'm that forgetful nooadays that I wid forget far I'd put the money. Aggie Dreep needed a hidey-hole for a chocolate gateau ae day so she jist laid it inside the tumble-drier, I believe. Only she forgot ti tell Walter and he threw in a load o' sheets athoot lookin and switched it on. What bonnie pattrens they got on their downie.

Onywye, the bobbies came roon efter ma burglary. Affa nice they were, considerin. "Fit his been tooken, ma dear?" he said. Educatit kinna blokie.

"I canna richt say," I telt him. "Nae nithing as far as I can see."

"So ye've jist been rummled aboot a bit?"

"That's aboot the size o't," I said.

Well," said the bobbie, "it disna gie us much help, bit folk lik that usually try twa or three places at a time, so we'll get back in touch wi ye if we hear onything. Div ye wint wir security boys oot? They'll gie ye free advice."

So I'd the security boy oot fae The Toon the next Thursday. He wis an affa nice blokie. Affa sympathetic. He said he widna recommend affa expensive stuff because he kent I wis jist on the pension, and he didna like til alarm me or onything, bit lichtnin rarely strikes in the same place twice, he said.

"A good job," I said, "because if he shows his face in ower my door again I'll kick his erse twice roon the gairden and oot intil the road.

He said he admired ma spirit, bit he wisna sure that wis a good idea.

Lo and behold, three wikks efter that I wis up for jury duty. I got a letter in the post askin if I wid report for jury service a few wikks later. Now, I'd aye wintit ti be on a jury. I richt likit that Perry Mason on the TV, so I phoned the lady at the coort and I says: "Jist you try and stop me."

So that wis how I endit up sittin in the coort a few wikks efter, in ma best coat, waitin for a shout fae a court clerk.

So I sat there and I sat there and I wisna gettin ony word. Nae official wis lookin the road o' me. The ither folk sittin roon aboot me didna look affa suitable for a jury in my opinion. I studied them real close. Affa roch-lookin billies. Jeans and smokin fags and chawin bubble-gum and a'thing. A richt menagerie.

Then this young lad gets up and he comes across and he says: "And fit hiv you deen, darlin? Fiddled yer meter?"

Well, hid I nae been sittin in amon a' the criminals? I shiftit oota that seat double-quick, I can tell ye. I found a coort usher and she said I'd been mis-directit and wid I go doon this corri-dor. So doon I goes.

Ae thing led til anither and I ended up on some kinna short-list. And wid ye believe it, by sheer coincidence, the case involved twa young loons that supposedly broke intil pension-ers' hooses a' ower Aiberdeen and pinched their savins. My bleed wis bilin, — let — me — tell — you.

Then the sheriff askit me up and he says: "Madam," he says, "as this is a particularly testing case I must depart from customary procedure and ask you a few questions to establish your suitability as a potential juror."

"Ask awa, your honour," I says.

"Have you formed any opinion about the innocence or guilt of the young men on trial?"

"Not a bit," I says.

"Good," he says, "and for our guid-ance, do you have any objection in principle to custodial sentencing — that is, a prison term — should it become necessary after the case?"

"No," I said. "Nae for twa little buggers lik this."

**BARBARA FLORENTYNA MCTAVISH GIRN (68)**
**does not suffer fools gladly and is a woman of firm opinions and brusque manner when required.**
**She finds it particularly hard to cope with snobbery and affectation, which sets her on a collision course with Mrs Kate Barrington-Graham more frequently than not.**
**Despite this, Mrs Barrington-Graham has tried several times to make peace, most notably when Mrs Girn's tattie-pot turned out to be a valuable piece of renaissance porce-lain worth thousands of pounds.**
**Mrs Barrington-Graham called, hoping for a peep at such a marvel-lous piece, and invited Mrs Girn to attend her daughter's "coming-out".**
**Mrs Girn was unimpressed; said: "I didna even ken she wis in the jile", and shut the door.**

31

# Ebenezer Grip

❝My favourite place is nae a secret ata. My favourite place is slap-bang aside ma till in the Stronach Emporium and General Stores. The very spot I've stood at this last sixty-five year, and far ma faither stood for forty year afore that. That's the spot that I've served generations o' folk at Stronach fae, and that's the spot far I've made a' ma money. Are ye surprised that I've got a saft spot for it?

I wid say that I've aye been a trader by nature. It's ma instinct. It's in ma bleed, as ye micht say. Some folk hiv the knack and some folk hinna. I think I've got it. I'm a natural-born salesman.

I canna say there's ony secret, really. Sellin *is* an art. If ye're lookin for hints or tips, the best advice I can offer ye is that ye should 'always look sincere'. Even if ye dinna mean it.

Dinna think my kinna success comes overnight. There's a lotta hard work in front o' ye if ye're thinkin o' a career in sellin or retailin. Money disna jist roll intil yer lap. And ye'll hae a few disasters along the road. I hid my fair share o' financial trugedies, bit I nivver saw them as trugedies; I saw them as opportunities.

Fit is it they say? The person that didna mak a mistake didna mak onything? That's really true. Learn fae yer mistakes and ye get stronger and better. That's the reason I'm a success noo. Mistakes.

Fit kinna mistakes?

Well, for instance, there wis the time in the early 1920s that I'd made a coupla bob wheelin and dealin here and there, so I thocht I wid surprise the femly wi a nice present. Ma mither and faither were baith alive at the time and we a' bed in the flat abeen the shop.

I puzzled for wikks aboot fit kinna surprise I wid get them. I thocht aboot a dog, bit I aye think a dog's an affa tie. And, onywye, a dog's jist an expense, and I widna be an affa great trader if I wis handin oot presents that jist cost folk mair money.

I thocht aboot claes, bit ma faither already hid his overall and his Sunday suit and he didna really need onything else. Ma mither wisna an affa dressy wifie, eether.

I thocht aboot flooers, bit flooers jist wither awa and ye're left wi nithing for yer money.

And then I hid ma great idea. Folk wis spikkin affa aboot gramophones at the time. Jist aboot ivry place that ye went ye heard the Charleston or some ither dance blarin oot o' ae horn or anither. And that wis the very thing. Ma folks wis baith real fond o' music. Ma mither wis an affa wifie for Caruso.

So I went til a lad I kent in The Toon and I socht a good price on the latest model o' gramophone. It hid a' the business. A little pottie for needles and a'thing.

"Ebenezer," he says, "for you, twinty poun."

Now, twinty poun wis twinty poun — a lotta siller in the 1920s. I could feel ma flesh rinnin caul wi the thocht o' spendin a' that siller in ae go. Fit if they didna like it?

Dash it, though, they'd been real good ti me, and I jist took it. It wis a real good deal, though I wis sweatin as I handed ower the big white fivers.

So I gets the trainie hame cairryin this great big box wi the horn stickin oot the tap, and I could see folk lookin at me and thinkin I must be real flush.

I cairried it up the road fae the station and intil the Emporium and I put it doon on the big table in the back shop. "There ye go," I says. "A present for yer anniversary."

What trickit they were. Lik twa kids in a sweetie shop.

"Foo much wis this?" said ma faither.

Well, I couldna tell him I'd spent twinty poun on a gramophone, so I jist telt him it cost me a fiver. That wye, he thocht I'd deen real weel in the tradin.

"We'll mak a shopkeeper o' ye yet," he said, and I wis real prood.

I went awa a coupla days later and fan I come back the gramophone wisna there. I lookit a'wye, bit I wis dashed if I could find it.

I wisna feart that it wis stolen, because we didna hae stealin at Stronach in the 1920s, so I jist asked ma faither and he said: "Well," he said, "we'd a fairmer in here this mornin and he offered us ten poun for it, so we jist took it.

"And he's needin anither sivven."

**EBENEZER JACOB SCROOGE GRIP (93) is the second-oldest person in the Howe of Stronach and is remarkable for the fact that he still runs the Stronach Emporium and Village Stores single-handedly, getting up at 6am every day and closing at 8pm.**

**Mr Grip knows the right side of a ha'penny. His financial prudence has long been celebrated throughout the howe, and there are few bargains to be had at the emporium, even at his comparatively recent forays into New Year sales.**

**As a distinguished resident of the vale, Mr Grip was asked to perform a naming ceremony for two of the new rowing boats at the Stronach Pleasure Park boating pond in the summer of 1987.**

**He caused some consternation when he found he could not bring himself to let go of the bottles of champagne.**

# Virginia Huffie

**"**I dinna think there's a corner at Stronach that I dinna like, if I'm honest, bit I've a special soft spot for Crochlie Neuk. The old folk's home, ye ken. It's nae that I'm hopin for a placie there; it's jist that it means a lot til me for private reasons. It wisna aye an eventide home, ye see. Back afore the war, it wis a wee hospital for folk wi "social difficulties", I suppose they wid ca it noo. Folk that couldna quite fit in.

I felt real sorry for them and I often took a tekkie ower on ma bike on ma day aff fae the kitchie at Wester Bogensharn. I'd maybe rummle up a puckle bannocks, cover them wi a dishtooel and crunk doon til the village.

It wis maistly blokies that wis in there. Fine lads, they were. They'd maybe jist gien aff the rails wi drink or maybe they'd some tragedy or sadness in their past and they maybe hidna coped wi it as weel as some o' the rest o's cope. Ye canna criticise them for that. It can happen til onybody.

I hid a real soft spot for Jimmy. He wis an affa Jimmy. A real educatit blokie, bit as daft as a nine-bob note. Ilky July, he wid be up in front o' the Social Board for an assessment for release. Three folk wid quiz him and a psychiatrist wid listen and then they wid decide if they could let him go. Usually, they wid decide they couldna.

I asked Jimmy ae day fit like questions they asked and he said they asked the queerest questions like: "If you were to be given a full discharge from this institution, what would be the first thing you would do?"

So I asked him fit his answer hid been. Ye ken fit he said? He said that he'd telt them: "I wid come back wi a catapult and I wid smash ivry windae in this affa place."

Well, ladies and gentlemen, is it ony winder that they widna let him oot? I telt him he should maybe reconsider bein as blunt as that fan he come up for his chunce the follyin year, bit Jimmy said he wis a man o' his principles and he couldna change his views jist for fower aul fogies in three-piece suits. I suppose ye can admire him for that, though he wis still daft as a nine-bob note, if ye ask me.

The next July, he wis up for his hearin again and I happened ti be there afore he went in. "Now, Jimmy," I says, "be a bittie mair careful wi yer answers this time and ye micht be lucky." He jist smiled at me and off he went.

Well, he wis back twinty minutes later wi a face on him like a flittin. "Nae luck, Virginia," he said. "I'm stuck in this place for anither year."

"Fit did ye say this time?" I asked.

"Jist the same," he said. "They askit fit I wid dee if I got oot and I said I wid come back wi a catapult and smash ivry windae in the place."

Well, I got really ratty wi him. "Jimmy," I said, "ye're yer ain worst enemy. Yer principles is a' very well, bit if ye're really needin oot o' this place ye really need ti play them at their ain game." I think he could see the sense o't.

The next year, I hid a good idea. I askit the board if I could sit wi Jimmy durin his hearin because I wis sure he wis gettin nervous and nae showin himsel at his best. They agreed. And that wis how I came ti be sittin in front o' the three big-wigs and the psychiatrist at Jimmy's third attempt.

"Now, James," said the consultant. "If we were to release you, what would be the first thing you would do?"

"I wid tak Virginia here oot for a meal ti say thank-you for her friend-ship," he said. Wisn't that affa nice o' him?

"And then?" said the doctor.

"And then I wid seek a lend o' ma brither's car and I wid ask Virginia if she wid like ti go for a drive in the country wi me."

The board wis lookin impressed, and I wis real touched masel.

"And then?" said the doctor.

"And then I wid stop at Potarch on Deeside and ask if she wid like an ice-cream."

"And after that, James?"

"Then I wid spread oot a travellin-rug on the bonnie green grass in front o' the hotel and I wid lie doon on it aside her."

I wis nearly blushin, I dinna mind admittin.

"And then, James? What would you do then?"

"I wid pit ma airms roon aboot her and squeeze her ticht as she gazed up at me."

"And?"

"Then I wid pull aff her corset, rip oot the elastic, mak a catapult and come back here and smash ivry windae in the place."

**VIRGINIA MARGARET MARY HUFFIE is one of Stronach's quieter souls. Never married, she has nevertheless maintained a wide circle of friends and is admired for her even temper and willingness to help.**

**She is a noted animal-lover and now has two cats — Piercy and Big Black Sambo — although in her past she had a menagerie of budgies, a dog, guinea-pigs, hens, tropical fish and a monkey. When the monkey and the dog died, she decided that she was becoming too old and so passed on all her pets bar her beloved cats to good homes.**

**She so revered the memory of the monkey and the dog, however, that she took them to a taxidermist.**

**"Do you want them mounted?" he inquired.**

**"If it's a' the same," she said, "I'd prefer them jist shakkin hands."**

# Erchie Sotter

“Now, here's a silly question. Far's my favourite place at Stronach? Need ye ask? There's only the one spot for me, and that's my special seat at the lounge bar at the Stronach Arms. Erchie's Perchie, the plaque says, in honour o' me bein their maist reg'lar customer.

Of course, me likin a drammie means I get affa bothered wi kirkie folk. Holy Wullies and that. They try ma door twa-three times a year, I suppose. There's aye somebody tryin ti mak me sign the pledge. I aye says I'm nae signin ony-thing athoot a lawyer present. Then, fin I hid ma hert attack a twa-three year ago, what excitit the Holy Wullies got. They were that keen that I should learn the error o' ma ways that they were visitin me in the hospital and a'thing. They were roon aboot ma bed in Forsterhill, lik flees roon a jeely piece, preachin and lecturing at me aboot the evils o' drink.

I mind this wife — a Mrs Cummine, I think — shouting at me wi a Bible in her hand aboot the demon drink and how it wis the demon drink that hid landit me in the hospital and how the demon drink wis causin a' ma problems and how it wis the demon drink and the demon drink alone that wid be my undoin eventually.”

Fit can ye say wi a ravin lunatic lik that at the fit o' yer bed?

I jist says: “Thanks for bein reassurin, Mrs Cummine,” I says. “It's richt fine hearin that the demon drink is causin a' ma problems. A'body else says it's ma ain fault.”

Ma son and his wife that hiv the boardin-hoose at Portsoy are gettin a bittie agitated aboot me, though. Evie — she's ma dother-in-law — she's begun nag-gin me aboot ma drinkin. They've even bocht me one o' that cassette courses in How to Stop Drinkin. I telt them I hidna time for listenin til cassettes. They said it wisna a cassette that ye sat doon and listened til. Ye played it ower and ower again at yer bedside and it wis guaranteed to stop ye drinkin while ye wis sleepin.

“Ye ken this, it works. I hinna hid a drink in ma sleep for wikks noo.”

It wis the hert attack that gave me the real scare, though. I wis jist walkin along the road ae day and I felt this tichtness aboot ma chest. I took a coupla mair steps and then the tichtness turned intil this sharp, jabbin pain a' ower ma body and doon ma airms. I jist fell doon a heap in the middle o' the road.

It took a whilie afore ony passer-by stopped and inquired if I wis a' richt. I suppose that's fan ye ken ye've got a reputation as a serious drinker.

Well, Stronach bein Stronach, in nae time ata there wis a crowd roon aboot, happin me up in blunkets until the ambulance or the doctor came. I canna mind right fit wis happenin.

Bit then I hears this little aul wifie shoutin: “Gie him a drappie whisky!”

And then somebody else shoutit: “Get him anither blunket!”

And then the little aul wifie shouts again: “Gie him a drappie whisky!”

And then I hears somebody else shoutin: "Hiv ye phoned for an ambulance?"

And then the little aul wifie shouts: "Gie him a drappie whisky!"

Then they a' startit argyin amon themsels aboot fit wis best for me, so I jist sat up, ill as I wis, and I said: "Wid a' you blighters shut up and listen til the little aul wifie?"

Of course, if I like a drink I canna tak a' the responsibility. It's that's easy got at nooadays, isn't it? And ye dinna like disappintin the bar staff, div ye? They're that hardworkin ye dinna like damagin their takins.

And they can be really helpful in yer hour o' need. Mony's a time I've relied on ma pals at the pubbie and ahen the bar ti help me oot o' a ticht spot. There's a comradeship, a camaraderie, in a Scottish pub that's nae like onything else on this earth. That's fit I cherish aboot ma visits til the pubbie. The friendship.

Ye wint a for-instance? I'll gie ye a for-instance.

The day ma wife died, I didna hae ony spare cash for a wreath. I didna. I wis that ticht on ma pension I couldna spare ony money. Bit I couldna let her go withoot a flooer, so far did I go for help? The social? The Kirk? The cooncil? Not on your nellie. I went til the pubbie.

"John," I says til the barman, "could ye gie's a lend o' £25 for a wreath for ma wife?" He went right intil his till, bit he wis nae lang opened that mornin so there wis jist £21 poun in it."

"That's OK," I says. "Jist gie's the £21, I'll tak the rest in Glenfiddich."

ARCHIBALD STOTT SOTTER (76) is a long-time Stronach resident and former railway shunter on the Stronach branch line.

A noted authority on the malt whiskies of Speyside, he can be found on most evenings at his stool in the public bar of the Stronach Arms Hotel.

Mr Sotter's health has been giving concern of late, to such a degree that he has been forced to attend the doctor's surgery by worried neighbours Mrs Barbara Girn and Miss Virginia Huffie.

The doctor advised that Mr Sotter's drinking habits would shorten his life, but that if he stopped drinking it would prolong his days.

Mr Sotter agrees. He stopped drinking for 24 hours and pronounced it one of the longest days of his life.

# Flo Spurtle

❝My secret place is a little walk I ken doon by the Water o' Stronach. I often go there if I feel life's gettin on top o' me. Well, ye need a placie ye can ca' yer ain, isn't that richt? I dinna go there as often as I used til. I'm mair settled in masel now that Gibby's got a job. He's the chief gairdener up at the Crochlie Neuk. Did ye ken? He's the only gairdener, of course, so I suppose it's richt enough that he's the chief gairdener. Titles dinna mean that much til him, but he wis that prood the day he got that job. I've nivver seen him sic happy. Tell ye the truth, I wis near greetin masel. I think he felt he'd really achieved something.

My Gibby's nae hid a lotta luck really. Nae luck richt fae the day he wis born. He wis fower month premature, ye see. He wis born in the July and his mither and faither got mairriet in the November. That's nae much o' a start in life that, is it?

It's nae that he's a bad husband. His hert's in the richt place, bit I aye think I hinna got a man and twa kids; I think I've got three kids. He taks as muckle lookin efter as Wayne and Cassandra. In fact, there's times I think he taks mair lookin efter than the twa kids put thegither. He needs savin fae himsel, Gibby. He lands in some affa scrapes.

I'm convinced they jist tak the lend o' him doon at the pub. There wis ae nicht he come hame and he wis certain that he wis relatit til the Royal Family. Doon at the pub, some o' the aul hands said they minded on some royal hinger-on drappin in by the pubbie ae day fan the aul king wis up at Balmoral and ae thing led til anither and Gibby wis the result.

Now, you and me wid ken a leg-pull, bit Gibby canna see it. He}s affa easy led. I says til him: "Gibby," I says, "the closest resemblance you've got til Royalty is King Kong." He wisna affa pleased.

Bit, like I say, his hert's in the richt place. He wid help onybody oot o' a jam. He winna see onybody stuck. There's times I think he's ower helpful, There's times there's nearly queues o' folk at oor hoose needin a haun wi something, or a shottie o' this or a len o' that. It gets on my nerves. Bit Gibby jist sails on, whistlin: *"If I can help somebody..."*

Erchie Sotter, he's the worst. He's forever roon by oor gairden shed needin a shottie o' something. I shouldna get involved, for they're nae my gairden tools, bit I dinna like seein ma man bein taen advantage o'. Ye ken fit I mean, ladies? Ye jist bile wi rage inside, div ye nae?

I said til Gibby ae nicht: "Gibby," I says, "D'ye nae think Erchie Sotter taks the len o' ye. He's forever sikkin a shottie o' yer rake, or yer hose, or yer shears. I widna mind, bit he nivver brings them back. Ye're aye chasin efter him for yer stuff. That's nae richt that. Ye should be a bittie firmer wi him."

Bit Gibby widna hear o't. "He's a neighbour and a frien," he said, "and if ye canna help a frien ye're nae muckle o' a man."

38

So I jist bit ma tongue. Ye canna argy wi him if he's in that kinna humour. Ye dinna get naewye if he's in a humour.

So I waitit ma time and a coupla nichts later, efter Erchie hid socht a shottie o' a graip, and I could see Gibby wis gettin a bittie fed up, I said: "Ye really need a plan," I said.

"Such as?" he said. "Nae maitter fit kinna plan I try, Erchie's quick-wittit. He'll aye get roon aboot me. I'm nae quick enough for him. There's nae pint tryin a plan. I'm as weel lettin him hae the tools if he wints them."

So I sat doon aside Gibby on the sofa. I felt real sorry for him. And I says: "Gibby," I says, "this is fit ye dee. The next time Erchie comes roon and he asks for, say, a shottie o' yer gairden hose, ye say: "I'm sorry, Erchie, I'm usin it the day, and the gairden's that dry that I'll be usin it for the rest o' the month at least."

A twa-three times o' that and he'll get fed up and leave ye be. I promise ye. Ye'll seen pit him aff wi a plan lik that.

So twa days later, Erchie turns up, bold as brass, at the gairden-shed door. "Gibby," he says, "it's an affa fine day. I wis jist windrin if ye'd be usin yer gairden hose this efterneen."

"Well," says Gibby, "as a matter o' fact, I am, Erchie. In fact, I'll be usin the hose for at least the rest o' this month. I'm sorry."

"Dinna you worry aboot that," said Erchie. "That's exactly fit I thocht, so ye winna be usin yer gairden shears. I'll jist tak them. Cheerio."

**FLORENCE SPURTLE (32)**
**has led a harassed life, despite her tender years. Her love affair with Gibby began early in primary school and, from then, her fate was sealed.**

**Mrs Spurtle's greatest moment of trauma came shortly after the birth of their son, Wayne, when she was wheeling him down Union Street, Aberdeen, in a baby buggy and Wayne swallowed a 2p piece, turned purple and began choking.**

**She pleaded and pleaded for help. Several people tried, but to no avail. Soon, Wayne had stopped breathing. Then a man in a mac strode forward, picked him up, bent him over and out popped the coin. Mrs Spurtle was immensely grateful and wondered how he had succeeded where so many others had failed.**

**"I am a tax inspector, madam,"**
**he said.**

39

# Gibby Spurtle

❝ There's really only one place I can pick as my special secret place in the vale and that's up ahen the bikesheds at the primary school. That's far me and Flo wis ... introduced ... as ye micht say. Man, I've some rare memories fae ahen the bikesheds. Happy days.

In fact, I enjoyed ma schooldays. I wisna affa clivver, I ken that. I wis aye near the bottom o' the class, bit that disna mean I didna enjoy the fitba and the raffia and the gairdenin. I still say it wis the school that startit me aff gairdenin. I suppose ye could say it wis the school that gave me my career, now that I'm heid bummer in the greenhoose at Crochlie Neuk. I can still mind the thrill o' ma first dreel o' tatties. I came top o' the class for that dreel o' tatties. That wis the first time I'd come upon something creative that I wis really good at; something that I wisna bottom o' the class at. I think that's affa important. A'b'dy maun hae something they can say they've maistered, I aye think.

Of coorse, I canna claim that it wis a' successful. I wis real hot on the practical side o' the gairdenin, bit the written exams jist conniched me. I could pit in tatties wi the best o' them, bit write aboot it on paper and I wis jist clean lost. In fact, I failed ma exam. It wisna really my fault. I got affa flustered in the exam room. Exam nerves, I suppose.

I still mind the question that sunk me. It wis aboot weeds and it askit if there wis "a foolproof method of telling whether or not a young plant is a weed or something to be cherished. Please elaborate".

Fit wis my answer? I said that if ye pulled up a'thing in the gairden, the stuff that grew back wis the weeds. I thocht it wis a real clivver answer, that.

Onywye, ye ken how, fin ye were at school and ye were sittin exams and ye came oot o' the exam hall and yer teachers were stannin there, bitin their nails and askin fit the exam paper hid been like? Well, I came oot o' the hall and the gairdenin teacher wis there and he says: "How did you get on, Gilbert?", so I telt him aboot the weeds question and the clivver answer I'd come up wi.

He startit greetin.

I wis affa embarrassed. I thocht at the time he wis jist overcome wi relief, bit now I ken he wis jist overcome.

Still, it hisna held me back, his it? Ma dad said I wis jist a waster. He said that ivry one o' ma classmates wid dee better in life than me because I wis ower lazy and ower stupid. It's affa fit some parents say til their kids, isn't it?

Onywye, we'd a school reunion in May and a' the folk in my class turned up, except the lad that emigratcd til Los Angeles and now he maks millions bein a lawyer til the stars — he wisna there.

Bit I bumpit intil ma best pal, Derek. I hidna seen him for years. We'd kinna lost touch. Derek wis aye a bit o' a whizz kid at the school — especially wi arithmetic — and he'd aye said his ambition wis settin up his ain business and makkin a million afore he wis twenty-one. Well, I strode intil the school and there he wis: pot-bellied and bald. "Hullo, Dek," I says, "foo's yer doos?"

What a scare I got wi him. Here wis a man the same age as me; usually life and soul o' the party, big ideas, burnin ambitions, clivver, and fit wis I seein at this reunion?

An aul mannie. An aul mannie o' thirty-four. He jist stood there, nae even able ti raise a smile.

"Oh, hullo, Gibby," he says. "Nae affa great, if ye must ken."

"Did ye achieve yer ambition?" I says. "Did ye set up yer ain business? Did ye mak yer million afore ye wis twinty-one?"

"Well, Gibby," he says, "I set up ma business. Bit ye ken how I fancied Fiona wi the legs at the school? I mairriet her, bit she ran aff wi ma business partner and they took a' the money we hid in the safe.

"I got mairriet again twa year later, bit ma second wife fell for a Spanish waiter and they ran aff til Barcelona.

"I thocht I wid mak a clean break so I bocht a little hoosie aside the sea. The cliff began subsidin and ma hoose fell intil the watter.

"Ye probably see that I walk wi a limp noo. I wis oot for a walk ae Sunday and I fell in a great big hole in the road and as I wis workin masel free a big van came by and flattened me. Sixteen broken bones and a fractured skull.

"Then yesterday, afore I came up here, ma dog ran oot in front o' a road-roller and ma motorbike wis set on fire by vandals."

"Michty, Dek," I says, "That's affa that. Fit line o' business are ye in onywye?"

He says: "I sell lucky charms."

**GILBERT ALBERT SPURTLE (34)** **was born and brought up at Stronach and has declared that he will never leave his home airt.**

**Plagued by chronic unemployment, he found his niche in life in 1991 as chief gardener at the Crochlie Neuk Eventide Home in the village.**

**Gilbert (or Gibby, as he is known in the village) is an extremely popular figure; always ready to lend a hand and willing to help anyone out of a spot, even at his own expense, but he is acknowledged to be not particularly sharp as far as grey matter is concerned.**

**Despite this, his wife, Florence, and children, Wayne and Cassandra, love him dearly.**

**One morning, he dropped some ice cubes on the kitchen floor, picked them up, rinsed them under the hot tap and spent an hour and a half trying to find them.**

41

# Wayne Spurtle

❝ I've got a lotta favourite, secret places roon aboot the village. Places that naebody else kens aboot. Places me and Puddick can play in wir gang.

Sometimes, if Puddick's nae allowed oot, I go aff masel and play. I often go aff masel. I like ma ain company. Ye get mair freedom that wye.

I go aff masel if I ken relations are visitin the hoose. I jist need a sniff o' an untie or grandma or uncle and I'm oot the door. Cheerio. Maybe it'll be ma grandma up fae Manchester or ma unties and uncles fae Aiberdeen or roon aboot. I canna be deein wi grandmas and unties and uncles. They're aye slubberin in aboot at ye and treatin ye lik a little kid. I'm *nine,* for ony sake. I'm nae a little kid.

Ma Untie Bella fae The Toon arrived at the hoose ae Sunday efterneen. She gets on ma nerves. She's nae mairriet and one look at her and ye can see the reason.

Onywye, he starts makkin jokes at me. "And are you married yet, Wayne?" she says, wi this smirk ower her face, is if she's bein clivver or funny.

"Nae yet," I says. "Yersel?"

She didna like it. Her lips went a' little and screwed up and she started glowerin at me. Some folk canna tak their ain medicine. So I thocht I wid keep goin as lang as I wis winnin.

"And ye hinna ony babies yet, Untie Bella?" I said.

"No, Wayne," she said. "But I keep looking under the gooseberry bush for one."

"If that's how ye go aboot it, it's nae surprise ye hinna got ony."

She didna like that, eether.

"You're a very cheeky young man," she said. "I wouldn't be at all surprised if you never find yourself a girlfriend."

"I've already got a girlfriend, Untie Bella," I said. "We're rinnin aff thegither at Christmas."

Then she started smirkin again, and she says: "Of course you are, Wayne. You and your little girlfriend are running off to the bright lights and the big city. Is she nine years old, too?"

"No, she's ten. I like an auler woman."

"I see. And what do you suppose you'll do for accommodation? It's very expensive, you know."

"Ach, we winna stick," I said.

"And what about jobs? And money? You won't survive for long in a strange place without money."

"We winna stick," I said.

"And what about babies?7 What happens if babies come along?"

"Well," I said, "we've been lucky so far."

That shut the aul dragon up.

I'm sorry, but I jist canna thole folk that keep tryin ti tell kids fit they should and shouldna dee. It's nae as if they mak a great job o' it themsels.

I wis walkin up the Main Street the ither day, jist ootside the Kirk, and the Minister wis deein his gairden. It's a gey roch gairden, if ye ask me. Nae nithing like my dad's gairden.

Well, the minister looked up and he says: "Good morning, Wayne," he says, "it's a long time since we've seen you in Sunday School."

I said that I kent it wis, bit I'd been affa busy lately.

"Too busy for the Lord, Wayne?" he says. "We are none of us too busy for the Lord."

Now, I ken that fine, bit I dinna need tellin fac the minister.

"Yes, Wayne," he said, "we need the Lord's daily guidance in all things so that we follow the correct path."

"Ycs, minister," I says, and that wis fan I spottit a £10 note flutterin past ma feet in the street. I clappit ma feet ower it and I pickit it up. The minister wis watchin me.

"That's a ten-pound note if I'm not mistaken, Wayne," he said.

I said that it wis.

"And what are you going to do with it?" he said.

It wis neena his business, really, wis it?

"Are you going to keep it?" he said.

"No," I said, "I winna keep it."

"That's a good boy," he said. "I am really pleased to hear that. I am proud of you."

"No," I said, "I'll *spend* it."

**WAYNE JASON DOMINIC SPURTLE (9)** is what is known in the North-east as a nickum, a mischievous fellow who is basically "a good loon".

Wayne is weathering severe parental pressure to begin thinking about a possible career, despite the assurances of his teacher, Miss Pink, that nine is a little early to be thinking of an adult future.

Florence, his mother, is concerned at his poor school reports and wonders what Wayne can do as a career if everything he tackles is inaccurate. He suggests a TV weatherman.

He has also asked if he could go for training as a park rubbish collector on the grounds that he wouldn't need training.

"Why would you not need training?" asked his father, Gilbert.

"Because," said Wayne, "ye jist pick it up as ye go along."

# The Rev. Montgomery Thole

❝ Quite clearly, my favourite little place in the whole of the Vale of Stronach has to be my pulpit. It gives me so much pleasure to know that much good is being done from such a small space and to know that I have some part in it. I cannot tell you what a thrill it is to know how much a few well-chosen and sincere words are able to give comfort and strength in times of crisis.

Now, I will be the first to admit that I was not an unqualified success when first I arrived in the community three or four years ago In fact, I suspect many of them were a little suspicious of me. Yes, suspicious. Can you believe it? Of me. I know now that overt friendliness — chumminess, I like to call it —is perhaps not something a small community in North-east Scotland expects from a man of the cloth. I found a tremendous reluctance by the parishioners to call me by my first name, for instance

"Call me Monty," I would say, but they could not bring themselves so to do. I tried a stage which was a little more formal "Call me Montgomery." But, no, they were happiest calling me Mr Thole then and they are happiest calling me Mr Thole now, and I expect we will remain on these frighteningly formal terms until the day comes to leave the charge.

Which is not to say that my parishioners cannot show a touching gesture if the opportunity arises. I recall a wedding last summer in which a farmworker and his bride were standing at the pulpit after they had slipped the rings on each other's fingers, I had blessed them and we had repaired to the vestry to sign the register.

"Mr Thole," said the groom (you see what I mean about formality?) "Mr Thole, we maun thank ye for deein wir weddin for us, especially wi us nae bein reg'lar kirkgoers, so I wid like ye til accept a payment for yer time and trouble. How much wid be richt, wid ye say?"

Now, wasn't that touching? There was no need, after all.

"Mr Robertson," I said. "Talk of money always embarrasses me. It's such an earthly thing, don't you find? Let's just say that you should give the Kirk funds what you think it was worth to you to have married Agnes."

Well, he thought for a few moments, bless him, and then he pulled out six £5 notes. He pressed the thirty pounds into my hand and I thanked him profusely. Then he turned to gaze lovingly at his bride and I was most thrilled to see a young man study his new bride with such seriousness.

Then he turned back and pulled £25 out of my hand and stuffed it back into his trouser pocket.

Of course, my community help is not limited just to performances of services. I find that I can be of immense help throughout the community in myriad small ways. For instance, do you recall those awful storms we had in March, 1992, when it seemed that half the North of Scotland might have been blown away? I'm sure that you do. How could we forget?

In any case, I happened to be walking along the Main Street in the village during one of these blustery squalls when a young lady stepped out of the post office and slipped on the wet pavement right in front of me. The poor young woman. How embarrassing.

Anyway, I strode right up to her as she lay there, sprawled on the paving stones, postal orders and stamps lying everywhere, and I held out my hand. That's all. I simply held out my hand.

She looked up at me with her beautiful eyes and I could see that she was grateful. You can in those circumstances, can't you?

However, I could see at the same time that she was mortally embarrassed, so I attempted to make light of a perfectly understandable accident by making my little joke about it. I always find a little humour eases the pain of the most awkward situations, don't you?

"My goodness, my dear," I quipped. "What an inclement day we are having. The weather is most inopportune and now you have had a minor accident befall you. Nevertheless, forget any embarrassment you might be feeling, for there is no need.

"And, after all, this is the first time I can say truthfully that I have picked up a fallen woman."

Well, how she laughed. Her eyes danced with laughter and gratitude.

"Why, thank you, minister," she said. "This is the first time I have been picked up by a man of the cloth."

**THE REV MONTGOMERY THOLE (40) was appointed to his charge at Stronach in 1990 and has settled in well to the life of the vale, although his unorthodox ministry has not been a universal hit.**

His theological tastes are little too contemporary for the liking of many of the older residents, but his reception among older people can be balanced by the enthusiasm of younger Stronach churchgoers, who find his modern outlook refreshing and his lighter approach to Christian worship a pleasant change, more in keeping with the times.

When a young couple approached him for spiritual counselling before their wedding this summer, they asked nervously if he approved of sexual relations before marraige.

"Well," he said, "only if it doesn't hold up the service."

# The
# Stories

# Erchie meets
# his match

*Episode 144 : July 28, 1990*

ANYONE visiting Stronach last Saturday evening would have found the village strangely quiet. Several coaches had taken virtually everyone in the howe to an Aberdeen hotel to celebrate the diamond wedding of two residents of the Crochlie Neuk eventide home, on the outskirts of the village.

After the meal, the Stronach contingent had got down to the serious matter of gossip and catching up on the private business of everyone else. Walter Dreep leaned across to Sandy Brose. "And fa's the dame ower in the corner?"

Sandy craned over Walter's shoulder and spied Erchie Sotter flirting shamelessly with a woman half his age. Erchie was smiling into her face and chatting animatedly while she, almost as intrigued, was laughing politely in all the right places.

Sandy smiled to himself and turned back towards Walter. "Her borin in aboot wi Erchie?" he said. "Her wi the fur coat and the joolery? Her wi the make-up and the high heels? Div ye nae recognise her?"

Walter tried a sneaky nonchalant look across the top of his glass, as if smoothing his hair and adjusting his tie, all at the same time. After a judicious period of study, he turned back. "Canna say as I div," he said.

"Babbie Girn's niece fae the Broch," said Sandy.

"Awa," said Walter, sneaking another look. "Nae little Ambrosia. It's nivver."

"The very same," said Sandy. "Ambrosia Girn. The one and only."

"My, my," said Walter, drinking in this vision of Buchan pulchritude. "I hinna seen Ambrosia in near twenty year. My, my. Ambrosia Girn. My, my, my." He studied for a few seconds longer.

"I say, she's fairly filled oot in a' the richt placics."

"And man-mad, I hear," said Sandy. "Nivver mind yer women's lib wi Ambrosia. She wis libbed lang afore onybody ivver thocht o' libbin. Erchie's bitin aff mair nor he can chaa there."

They watched Erchie and Ambrosia for virtually the rest of the evening. Only when Ambrosia left to powder her nose did they shout across: "Watch yersel thonder, Erchie; ye're nae the mannie ye were." But Erchie merely waved away the comment and grinned back.

A few hours later, the evening had drawn to a pleasant close and Erchie had decided to walk back to his digs with his sister-in-law in Ferryhill. He had had a most satisfying and rewarding time, he thought, and he smiled as he walked and decided how lucky he was to have such a charming manner with the ladies. And how lucky they were, too, of course.

But the farther Erchie got from the hotel, the colder and darker it seemed to become until, quite quickly, he began to feel more nervous than he would have liked. A pensioner alone in a big city needs to be careful, he thought to himself. When soon he approached the end of the dark lane down which lay his sister-in-law's house, he heard what he thought were drunken shouts coming from the far end.

He hesitated, suddenly nervy.

That was when he heard footsteps behind him. He froze, hardly daring to turn round. And the slow tap-tap of shoes became louder and louder until they stopped, right behind him. Erchie turned round slowly.

There was Ambrosia, laden with half-a-dozen parcels.

"Erchie," she said. "Are you staying down here?"

Erchie nodded, almost sighing with relief.

"So why are you not heading off?"

"Ach, jist takkin a breath o air," he said. "Ye ken fit like. Us chiels that likes keepin in trim needs wir exercise."

Another shout of young lads came from the dark at the far end of the lane and Erchie swallowed hard. Ambrosia, meanwhile, was studying him by the light of the street lamp. "Why, Mr Sotter," she said, "I do believe you're frightened."

"Awa ye go," said Erchie. "Me? A Desert Rat? Feart? I dinna ken the meanin o' the word. I'm nae feart." He stole a quick glance up into the gloom of the lane, then turned back. "Onywye," he said, sidling up to her, fit did I tell ye the nicht aboot me bein jist the chiel ti look efter a young lassie lik yersel? I couldna dee that if I wis feart at the least little thing noo, could I?"

"Well, you're hovering about here like a nervous kitten," said Ambrosia. "Tell you what. Would you like me to walk you down the lane to your back door?"

"Na, na," said Erchie, trying (and nearly managing) a nervous laugh. "I ken you young dames. Ye'll only try and tak advantage o' me. Me and ma manly charms."

"Erchie," she breathed again. "I ask you. How could I possibly take advantage of you? I'm carrying all these parcels. I'm so burdened that I couldn't even lay a finger anywhere on you. You have absolutely nothing to worry about, I do assure you."

Erchie thought for a moment.

"Well," he said, "I could easy cairry yer parcels."

# Gossip at the show

*Episode 149 : September 1, 1990*

THE first day of the annual Stronach Gala was a great success. As usual, tractors, floats and beasts were being shuttled around the village as early as 4.30am. The committee had been up until the wee sma oors with their final planning, confident that they had forestalled every possible problem.

Dispersed to their various homes around the vale, they were up again and reconvening at four (just to be on the safe side). They had laid on attractions, sideshows, demonstrations, free offers, games, sports, competitions and dozens of other entertainments,

The sunshine was baking. People were thronging in their hundreds around the showring, chattering and laughing with the excitement of it all. Children chased each other in and out of the marquees' guy-ropes. Had merciful fate decreed that just one of the agricultural shows in Scotland would be perfect in every way this season, it surely had picked the Stronach Gala.

Across in the tea marquee, scones risen to perfection were displayed next to bannocks which could not have been more deliciously golden, and jugs of creamy farm milk sat next to dishes of impossibly bright-red home-made strawberry jam.

Babbie Girn turned to Virginia Huffie. "Aye, the show's nae fit it wis."

"Oh?" said Virginia, surveying the happy crowds and allowing a look of slight puzzlement to cross her features.

"Na," said Babbie, sighing, "nae the same as it wis in oor day. That was fan a show really wis a show." She gazed dreamily into the middle distance while sucking softly on the last of her rock cake.

"A scone wis a scone in oor day. A bannock really wis a bannock. Ye could taste the jam. The milk wis that creamy ye nott a speen." She sighed fondly. "The sun wis aye shinin. The folk wis happy. Hunders o' folk lachin and enjoyin themsels. Aye, rare days."

Virginia peeped through the marquee flap at the sun shining, the people happy, the folk laughing and enjoying themselves. She wondered to herself, but she knew better than to say anything.

"Weel," said Babbie, suddenly snapping out if it, "dash it, I'm a thochtie dry, Virginia. We maun nip ower til the bar tent for a something lang and cool. Fit aboot a sweet stout?"

"That sounds rare," said Virginia, gathering up her handbag and cardigan. And off they set.

ACROSS in the bar, Babbie and Virginia fought through crowds of farmers and young bucks to plonk themselves in front of the trestle table. But the barman, whose face Babbie didn't recognise, seemed to be intent on serving all the farmers and farm workers before he paid any attention to her.

"Excuse me," she said. But he ignored her.

"Excuse me," she said again, a little more loudly.

Still nothing.

"Hey, min," she shouted. The barman turned round and looked at her. "Aye, you," said Babbie. "The barman. I've been waitin here a whilie noo. Ye maybe hinna noticed me; I'm only twelve steen and I'm easy missed. Onywye, fin ye've finished servin a' this fairmers, if it's quite OK wi you and it disna interrupt yer plans, I'll tak twa sweet stouts fae ye and be snappy aboot it."

The barman smiled to himself, but still did not apologise. He reached down into a crate for a couple of bottles of stout. He prised off the tops; sat two glasses on top of the bottles, and pushed them forward.

"Three pound fifty, love," he said in a strong Cockney accent.

Babbie and Virginia gasped. "Three poun fifty?" said Babbie. "I askit for twa bottles o' stout, nae twa bottles o' chumpagne."

"Two bottles of stout," he said, pushing them a little closer to Babbie, "is exactly what you've got, love. Three pound fifty, please."

"Three poun fifty," said Babbie, aghast. "Awa and chaw yer lugs. That's daylight robbery, that." Her eye caught a sign on one of the marquee poles. "There ye go," she said. "The sign up on yer post says this is the Happy Hour."

"Well," said the barman, "I'm pretty happy. Three pound fifty."

Babbie could feel the heat rising in her hairnet and the blood coursing slightly faster in her veins. "Ye're nae fae hereaboots," she said, fixing him with a determined stare as she rummled about in her purse.

"No, lady," said the barman. "I ain't. Londoner, born and bred. And proud of it."

"Well, Lord help yer wife, that's a' that I can say," and Babbie slapped three pound coins and a 50p piece on to the table.

"Sorry, lady," said the barman, gathering up the coins. "I ain't married. Free and easy. Footloose. Bachelor all me days."

"Aye, well," said Babbie, turning to go, "if it's good enough for yer faither, it's good enough for you."

# Return of the wanderer

*Episode 167 : December 29, 1990*

T HE urgent knock at Babbie Girn's front door on the morning of Christmas Eve did not find her in the best of humours. She had sent 27 Christmas cards, but had received in return only 25. The post had come and gone and there was no sign of the dilatory two, so she had cleared the lot off her sideboard and had sat down to compare the pile with her list to establish who would be removed from her Christmas-card list for next year.

When she opened the door, there stood a tall, portly man in his late forties or early fifties. He sported calfskin boots, a pale-blue suit and a stetson. Behind him stood a woman in her mid-forties, dressed in similarly unrestrained style.

"Aye?" barked Babbie, but the couple just stood smiling and grinning.

"Well?" said Babbie. "Are ye needin something? I hinna a'day. "

"Doncha know us, Babbie?" drawled the man.

Babbie screwed up her eyes a little more and peered at them. Evidently, she didn't know them.

"It's us," said the would-be cowboy. "Bert and Pansy. Your nephew and niece. Over from the States for Christmas in the old country."

"Bert and Pansy?" said Babbie, screwing up her eyes even tighter. "Bert and Pansy? Nae Bert and Pansy fae Lonmay?"

"Abilene, Texas, now ma'am. Ain't been near Lonmay since we left in sixty-four."

"Weel, weel," said Babbie, "Bert and Pansy. Bert and Pansy. Weel, weel, weel." She stood to one side. "Weel, seein as ye're a' the wye fae Texas for yer fly, ye'd better come in, I suppose. It winna be nithing funcy, mind. It'll be a buttery and syrup."

Bert and Pansy strode into the house.

Babbie, meanwhile, took the staff of a brush and rapped it against the window of her next-door neighbour. When Virginia Huffie came to her door, Babbie hissed at her to come round quick.

After a few moments, Virginia duly appeared and Babbie drew her aside in the lobby. "Look," she whispered, "there's twa folk inside. A coupla richt spongers hame fae the States. Bert and Pansy. Keep them spikkin gaun I mak a fly, will ye? And watch ma ornaments. Keep yer een on them ivry second. And try and be a bit livelier nor usual. Dinna show me up."

Babbie half-pushed Virginia into the living-room, where Bert and Pansy were standing politely beside the sofa. She introduced Virginia and went off to the kitchen. Virginia did her best to keep the chat going, but felt well out of her depth and, after five minutes, decided to venture to the kitchen to see if Babbie needed help.

"They seem a nice enough pair," said Virginia quietly.

"Chaw yer lugs," said Babbie. "That dame ben there didna *go* til America. She wis *sent* til America."

"Oh," said Virginia.

"Aye," said Babbie. "Her femly couldna thole a' the men she draggit hame. Ilky nicht a different lad. And aye wi his face covered in her lipstick. Man-mad, did ye say? There wis mair fingerprints on Pansy than Scotland Yard hiv in their files." Babbie put the lid back on the tin of syrup, arranged the butteries on a side plate and then turned to Virginia.

"That dame," she said, "his been on mair laps than a serviette."

"Oh," said Virginia, and she paused while Babbie loaded the tray. "He seems a nice blokie, though."

Babbie stopped again. "And he's exactly the same," she hissed. "A richt pair, they were. It maun be something in the watter at Lonmay. Couldna keep his hands aff onything in a skirt. A richt brither and sister they were. What sair herts they gave their mither. And her sic a nice wifie."

"Is that richt?" Virginia said.

Babbie strode back to the living-room. Virginia toddled behind her carrying a packet of custard creams.

"Well, Bert," said Babbie, unloading the milk and sugar. "It's funny ye took ycr sister wi ye and nae yer wife. Is she at hame in America?"

"Yup," said Bert. "She don't like flyin. But, man, she sure loves keepin house. You ain't never seen such a clean house, Aunt Babbie. She ain't never finished scrubbin and polishin and cookin and tidyin."

"Well, that's handy for ye," said Babbie. "And hiv ye femly yet?"

"Sure do," said Bert. "Left the little woman at home looking after the brood. She and I got us triplets. Three at once. Saves a lotta trouble, y'know."

"Oh, triplets," cooed Virginia. "What rare."

"Yup," said Bert proudly. "You know. They say it happens only once every ten thousand times."

"Michty," said Virginia. "It's amazin yer wife hid ony time for hoosework."

# Birds and bees

*Episode 177 : March 2, 1991*

WHILE she is a forward-thinking teacher, Miss Euphemia Pink of Primary Five at Stronach Primary is still wrong-footed occasionally by some of her pupils. This week, in an afternoon poster-painting session, with a buzz of activity in the classroom, Wayne Spurtle suddenly put up his hand, snapping, to ask an urgent question.

"Yes, Wayne," said Miss Pink. "What is it?"

"Please, Miss," said Wayne. "Fit's sex?"

Miss Pink stopped. "Pardon me, Wayne?" she said, although she had heard him perfectly well.

"Fit's sex?" said Wayne again.

The buzz of activity in the class faded away to an interested murmur. Thirty inquisitive heads turned to watch Miss Pink's reaction.

"Well, Wayne," she said, "I wonder what you're expecting me to tell you."

"Jist tell me fit sex is, please, miss," said Wayne.

"I'll tell you what," said Miss Pink, picking up some poster paints and moving back to the front of the class. "Come and have a word with me after school and we'll discuss this."

For the rest of the afternoon, Miss Pink's mind was rarely on teaching her class. Instead, she was working out a strategy for handling Wayne's somewhat blunt query.

She wondered if she should call in the headmaster, but decided against that. Instead, she would call in her colleague from Primary Seven, who seemed to have more experience of handling these delicate matters.

At 3.30, Wayne was soon alone in the classroom as all his chums left to go home, to football or to drama club. Miss Pink sat on the front edge of her desk and was soon joined by her colleague. Wayne sat there, perfectly composed.

"Now Wayne," said Miss Pink. "You'll be wondering why Miss Dicht is with us. Well, the reason is very simple. You see, she might know the answers to some questions that I don't know. And I might know the answers to some questions she doesn't know. That makes good sense, now, doesn't it?"

Wayne nodded.

"Wayne, I have always believed in telling the truth. You know that, don't you?"

"Aye," said Wayne.

"And I think that if a young man is old enough to ask a question, he should get an honest answer. You know that, too?"

Wayne nodded.

"So," said Miss Pink, and she began a long and detailed explanation of the birds and the bees, boy meets girl, and mummies and daddies.

Twenty minutes later, Miss Pink was flushed with the strain of it all; Miss Dicht nodded approvingly at her for a job handled sympathetically and delicately, and Wayne sat there nonplussed by all this new and intriguing information.

"Now," said Miss Pink, wiping her palms across the front of her skirt. "Does that help you?"

"Nae really," said Wayne.

Miss Pink and Miss Dicht stopped, puzzled.

"Not really," said Miss Pink.

"Nae really," said Wayne.

"Why is that?" said Miss Pink.

"Well, there's nae enough room."

"Not enough room for what?" said Miss Pink.

"Nae enough room for a' that birds and bees stuff on the entry form," said Wayne, lifting a newspaper cutting from inside his painting folder.

Miss Pink stepped forward for a closer look. It was an entry form for a children's painting competition in the Press and Journal.

"Ye see?" said Wayne, pointing to the cutting. "It says here: Name, Address, Age ... and Sex."

# A Gype calls

*Episode 183 : April 13, 1991*

THE tourist season at Stronach is already under way. Bolder travellers who like to venture from the well-trodden path often find themselves in the vale. So the time has come for Ebenezer Grip to dust down his "Special Prices for Tourists" sign and stick it in the window of Stronach Emporium and General Stores. The prices are special because they are twice the usual.

Last Wednesday, a large elderly man sporting a 10-gallon hat and a fat cigar strolled into the shop. After a few minutes getting his bearings, he strode up to the counter with outstretched hand. Ebenezer looked at the proferred hand with some bewilderment but, slowly, he took it and shook tentatively.

"Mighty nice to know you, sir," said the American. "My little lady and me are over looking up our ancestry and we figure we got us some Scotch blood. Clartmeyer's the name. Wilbur Clartmeyer, from Cicero, Indiana."

"Grip," said Ebenezer, hesitantly, and still shaking the hand. "Ebenezer Grip from Stronach, Scotland."

"So have you heard of my ancestors?" said the American, releasing Ebenezer's hand and putting his thumbs inside the top of his trousers, underneath an ample midriff. "Clartmeyer. Wilbur Clartmeyer. Cicero, Indiana."

"No," said Ebenezer, "I canna say as we've mony Clartmeyers hereaboots. There's a puckle Reids and Buchans; a fyow Forbeses and Gordons. We're clean deen o' Clartmeyers ivnoo, though."

"Say, that's real sad," mused the American, stroking his chin. "Real sad. I'd give just about anything to find my roots. Roots is real important. We got us all the time in the world and a whole mess of money to help us do it, too. Yes, sir, a whole mess of money."

"Ye widna be relatit til the Clartmeyers fae ower Rhynie wye, by ony chunce?" said Ebenezer quickly.

"Could be, could be," said the American, brightening. And then began a long discussion of the possibility of blood links between Cicero, Indiana, and Rhynie, Aberdeenshire.

"Well, Mr Grip," said the American eventually, "you've sure been a great help. Yes, sir, a great help." He thought for a moment. "Say! Do you suppose we got us a tribe?"

"A tribe?" said Ebenezer.

"Yeah," said the American. "A tribe. With a tribe chief and bagpipes and kilts and stuff."

"Oh, a clan!" said Ebenezer. "Well, I'm nae richt sure there's a Clartmeyer clan." He paused for a moment. "Hing on a mintie. There's maybe something in the Clan Directory."

Ebenezer stepped through the doorway to the back shop and half-turned to the left. Perfectly aware that the American's rapt gaze was following his every move, he half-hid the phone book so that Wilbur Clartmeyer could see only that it was an unknown volume of some substance. Ebenezer milked the intense gaze for a few moments longer, muttering: "Clartmeyer... Clartmeyer... Clartmeyer..." as he flicked through the pages.

"Here we go!" he said suddenly. "Clartmeyer." He read the supposed entry silently for a few moments then closed the books and walked back through. "Well, ye're nae a clan. Ye're a sept."

"A sept," mused the American. "We're a sept. Well, ain't that sump'n. A sept. I'll be darned.' He thought for a moment. "Say, what's a sept?"

"It's like a division o' a clan," said Ebenezer. "A branch o' a femly tree, if ye like."

"Oh, sure... sure..." said the American, considering these new implications. "So... so if we're a... a sept... does that mean we got us a clan also?"

Ebenezer thought quickly. There was still a substantial bankroll in the American's pocket. "Aye," he said, faltering only slightly. "Ye're a sept o' the... the... ye're a sept o' the Gype clan."

He brightened. "Aye, the Gype clan's yer clan, and nae mistake."

The American was suddenly brimful of the excitement of discovery. He reached forward and grasped Ebenezer by both shoulders. "Mr Grip. You've done me a great service, sir. You don't know how much this means to me. Suddenly to discover my roots after all these years."

"Well," said Ebenezer, trying to look modest about the supposedly great service he had bestowed. "Ye ken fit like. If I can help somebody..."

"And, sir, you've sure been a great help to me. Yes, sir. A great help. And I'd like to show my appreciation."

Ebenezer's eyes twinkled imperceptibly. "Wid ye now?" he said, rubbing his palm down the side of his grey-nylon overall to absorb a sudden sweat.

"I sure would," said the American. "I'd like to buy me a sample of our clan colours."

Ebenezer was wrongfooted for a moment. "Yer clan colours?"

"Sure thing," said the American. "You know. The stuff they make kilts out of. Plaid. My clan colours."

"Oh, yer tartan," said Ebenezer. The American nodded eagerly.

Ebenezer thought for a second. Tartan was something he didn't stock and, suddenly, he saw an opportunity vanishing. Then he spotted a lone tartan tin of Speyside shortbread on a far shelf. He started towards it.

"Well," he said, keeping his back to the American as he took it down. "I hidna really intendit pairtin wi this. It's a femly heirloom. A collector's item, really." He scraped desperately at the price label, which read £4.75.

"That don't matter," said the American pulling out the bankroll. From the corner of his eyes, Ebenezer could see him peeling back note after note. Ebenezer turned and walked back. He dusted the tin with the sleeve of his overall and placed it on the counter.

"And this is the Gype tartan?" said the American, now positively glowing. Ebenezer sighed, as if reluctant to see it go, and nodded slowly. "That's the Gype tartan," he said.

"Well," said the American, "I gotta have it. Name your price, Mr Grip. I *gotta* have it."

"Well, like I say, it's a collector's item," said Ebenezer. "Sentimental value. A rarity." He stroked his chin, then slapped his hand back on the counter.

"Dash it, I like yer face, Mr Clartmeyer. Seein as it's yersel, ye can hae't for ninety Scottish pounds."

The American pulled off five £20 notes with great speed and thrust them into Ebenezer's hands."Mr Grip," he said, "I like you, sir. Yes, sir, I like your style. Take the hundred."

Ebenezer stuffed the notes quickly into his hip pocket as Wilbur Clartmeyer picked up the tin of shortbread, gazed at it lovingly and made slowly for the door. As he half-opened the door and the little bell pinged, he turned back. "Mr Grip, I thank you, sir. I will always remember this day."

He looked fondly round the shop. "This is the day that I can say at last that I know who I am. I know where I have come from. I have connected with my ancestry. My heritage is mine once again. I have reclaimed my past. Yes, sir, I am whole. I am complete, as you might say. I, Wilbur Clartmeyer, of Cicero, Indiana, am complete. And at last, I know that I am a Gype."

"Aye," said Ebenezer. "Ye're a complete Gype, richt enough."

# Burgled!

*Episode 190 : June 1, 1991*

THE recession appears to have reached as far as Stronach and Ebenezer Grip, owner of the Emporium, suffers more than most. On Monday, the village awoke to find posters in the Emporium windows."Bargains! Bargains! Bargains!" they sang. "20% off everything! Ridiculous prices!"

The first day's takings were respectable enough. The till was slightly fuller than is usual for a Monday, although not quite as full as Ebenezer had hoped, and he went to bed only moderately happier.

Much worse lay in store, however, for he was awoken in the early hours by thumps and bumps from the shop below. He rose, went to the bedroom door and opened it slightly. Hearing hushed voices, he went back to his bedside and phoned the village bobby. By the time a sleepy constable turned up, 20 minutes after, it was too late. The bobby didn't even have to knock; he walked in through the back shop, where the door had been burst from its lock.

THAT morning the signs in the Emporium window had changed. "Closed due to Bereavement," they read. Opinions in the village were many and various. "Professionals," thought Erchie Sotter.

"Toonsers," ventured Sandy Brose, "they're a' the same."

"An inside job," thought Babbie Girn. "I ken an insurance fiddle fan I see't."

"I hear he's lost near twa thoosan pounds worth o' stuff," said Flo Spurtle.

"I heard nearer ten thoosan," said Virginia Huffie.

Only Dorothy Birze thought to see how Ebenezer, in his torment, was faring. She took a 10-minute walk from the pensioners' club to the emporium and knocked gingerly at the door of the back shop, which had been repaired.

It took Ebenezer a few minutes to shuffle to the back door. When confronted by Dorothy, his heart sank. "Are ye a' richt, Mr Grip?" she inquired sweetly.

"Terrible," said Ebenezer, making to shut the door again.

But Dorothy persisted. "Some fowk hiv nae respect for ither fowk's property," she said.

"Richt enough," said Ebenezer.

"Still, there's ae consolation," said Dorothy.

Ebenezer paused for a moment. "There is?" he said. "Fit's that?"

"It could hiv been a lot waur if it hidna been yer sale. At least a'thing wis twenty per cent aff."

# Desire rekindled

*Episode 196 : July 13, 1991*

IT WAS a somewhat shame-faced Genena Brose who crept into the doctor's surgery for her 5.45 appointment on Monday at teatime. The doctor motioned her to the seat at the side of his consulting table and she sat down and fumbled with the straps of her handbag.

Before he had time to say: "What can I do for you today, Mrs Brose?", Geneva announced: "I'm nae here for masel, doctor. This is nae for me, this."

"It's not?" said the doctor.

Geneva shook her head. "No, it's nae."

"So on whose behalf are you here?" said the doctor.

"It wis Miss Huffie — Virginia Huffie — that suggestit I come ower and see ye. And it's nae for her, eether. She's richt as rain. No, it's nae for her."

"So who *is* it for?" repeated the doctor, looking at his watch.

Geneva paused for a moment, as if burdened by second thoughts, then she drew the chair in a little closer, leaned forward and whispered: "It's ma man."

"Sandy," said the doctor.

"Ma man," confirmed Virginia. "He's nae himsel."

"He's ill," said the doctor.

"Is he?" said Geneva with a start.

"No," sighed the doctor, "I'm asking: 'Is he ill?' "

"Nae in as mony words," said Geneva. "He's jist nae himsel."

"For how long?" said the docor, scribbling a note on his deskpad.

"Aboot eicht year," said Geneva, peering at the pad and nodding.

"Eight years," said the doctor, looking up and squinting over the top of his half-moon glasses.

"Aff and on," said Geneva.

"What's the trouble?" asked the doctor, and Geneva shifted uneasily and nervously in her chair, as if reluctant to go further.

"You can tell me quite confidentially," he said.

"Well," said Geneva. "He's lost interest in me."

She waited to see the doctor's reaction, but he showed none, so everything else came spilling out in a verbal torrent of relief.

"He disna show me nae affection," she said. "He jist turns his back on me. He's nae the same. I ken I'm nae a strip o' a quine ony mair, doctor, bit I'm still a full-blooded woman. I've still got ma needs. Bit he's tired a' the time.

60

There's nae spark aboot him. Nae bosies. If I could trade him in lik an aul car, I wid. Bit he's ma man, so I canna."

By the end of it, she was relieved, but on the point of tears. The doctor pulled a paper hankie from the box on his desk. Geneva blew her nose with a loud rasp.

The doctor considered for a few moments. "This might sound strange, Mrs Brose," he said, "but the problem of which you speak is not as uncommon as perhaps you think. Pharmaceutical companies have been devoting a great deal of time and money into exhaustive research. And what they have come up with are these."

He showed Geneva a picture of a scatter of scarlet tablets. "They're the very latest thing," he said. "And I'm going to give you a few of these new tablets for Mr Brose to try."

The doctor began writing out a prescription. "They're quite an advance on previous medication available to GPs. They should perk him up a bit."

Geneva's eyes brightened and her face widened into a teary smile.

A FEW mornings later, Geneva turned up at Virginia Huffie's house collecting for the Retired Grieve's Benevolent Fund. Virginia was peeping from behind the net curtains and noticed that Geneva was stepping somewhat brightly and gingerly up the path.

On the knock-knock-knock, she went to the door and bade Geneva enter. Geneva almost shuffled through to the living-room; manoeuvred herself into position over the easy chair and let herself fall into it. She let go a heavy sigh.

"Ye're affa sair-made lookin," observed Virginia, as she fumbled in the top drawer of the sideboard for her spare-change purse.

"I'm near at the end o' ma rope," confessed Geneva, shifting uneasily in the easy chair as she tried to find a comfier position. "My Sandy's turned intil a tiger."

"A tiger?" said Virginia, stopping her search momentarily, for this was, indeed, a revelation.

"A tiger," confimed Geneva. "What a transformation. A wikk ago, I could hardly keep him fae sleepin by the fireside. Now I canna keep him in ae place for five minutes. What active he's become, Virginia. I canna keep tee til him. What a handfae."

She paused. "I got peels for him fae the doctor, ye see. Perky-up peels." Then she sighed. "Virginia, atween you and me, I could see that peels far enough."

Virginia found the purse and trotted round to the other easy chair to hear more.

"The doctor fairly said they wid perk him up a bit," said Geneva, "Bit I jist thocht he meant they'd mak Sandy a thochtie less sleepy or something.

"Perk him up? I'll say they've perkit him up. It's lik bidin wi Casanova and Valentino a' wrappit up in the ae man."

61

Virginia's nostrils flared imperceptibly and she smoothed down her tweed skirt.

"Ye dinna sound affa happy," she said.

"Well, some wyes I'm happier nor I wis," said Geneva. "Ither wyes I'm jist dirt deen. I'm nae as young's I wis, Virginia. I'm fifty-three. If I see fifty-four, I'll be lucky."

"It canna be that bad, surely," said Virginia, fumbling for a 50p.

"I'll tell ye foo bad it is, Virginia," said Geneva, leaning forward slightly, but grimacing with discomfort as she did so. "I'll tell ye foo bad it is.

"The doctor said ti me, he said: 'Give him one tablet daily, after meals', he said. Well, I slippit a puckle in his egg and chips yesterday at dennertime."

"And?" said Virginia.

"And I slippit anither couple in his mugga tea. Jist for bein sure, ye understand."

Virginia nodded.

"Well," gasped Geneva. "He took a moofae o' chips and then he jist froze. In nae time at ata, his heid fell back; his een rolled roon and roon; he let oot this growlin roar, and then he startit shakkin. Great big huge shaks, they were. Shak, shak, shak."

And Geneva shook just to convey the full power of Sandy's transformation.

"Shakkin lik that," she repeated.

"Michty," said Virginia. "And him eatin his denner."

"Well," said Geneva, "he loups oot o' his seat and lunges at me and he pits his airms roon aboot me and he starts kissin intil me and makkin slubbery noises and yellin lik Tarzan and standin on the seats and a'thing. Cutlery and plates fleein a'wye."

"Ooh," said Virginia, quivering. "Animal passion."

"I ken," said Geneva. "It wis affa. Really terrible. I winna be able ti show ma face in Littlewoods restaurant again."

# Sammy on wheels

*Episode 201 : August 17, 1991*

SINCE graduating from Aberdeen University last month, young Sammy Dreep has had a pretty lean time of it. With no job, and no prospect of one, time has lain heavily on his hands. He has helped his father, Walter, with the gardening until the garden has been worthy of anything produced at Beechgrove. He has helped the neighbours fill in their insurance forms and write official letters. He has gone for long walks around the vale to fill in the time, but to little avail. Unemployment is a hard beast to bear.

"I canna find a job if I'm nae mobile," he pronounced firmly at the tea table one evening this week. "Ye need mobility if ye're lookin for a job."

"Here we go again," said Aggie, putting down her knife and fork, as if to stress that her next homily was to carry extra gravitas. "Ye're — nae — gettin — the — car. Is that understood?

"That's a valuable car, that. I ken young loons. Five minutes inside that car and ye'll be rippin up the road showin aff. Na, na. Jist tak the bus and like it."

"It's nae an affa good bus service hereaboots," mumbled Walter through a mouthful of yellow fish. "The loon's got enough obstacles gettin a job athoot us addin til them."

"I see," said Aggie, "we're takkin sides noo, are we? Well, that car's nae for a young loon. A young loon needs a banger for startin aff. Nae a flash car lik oor Ford Escort. I ken him. He'll hae a' the young quines in the vale in that car. Well, nae in *my* car he's nae. Na, Na.

"Michty, he jist passed his test five month ago. Ten minutes in ower that car and he'll be in the ditch. Next thing we ken, he'll be up in the coort in front o' a judge. And the judge'll be sayin what a bad home he obviously came fae and what on earth wis his parents thinkin o' pittin him oot in a powerful car like that. Sammy'll end up in the jile. Oor names'll be plastered a' ower the daily paper. The hale village will be haein a richt gweed lach at us. We'll be black affrontit. And we'll nivver live it doon. I winna be able to haud up ma heid at the Rural again. Bang wid go my chunce o' bein group president. Sammy hisna the experience for handlin a powerful car lik that."

"It's a 1.3 Escort," said Sammy.

"Disna maitter," said Aggie. "It's far too powerful for a young loon. The answer's no. If I get an inklin that you've been ahin that wheel, ye'll hear o't. That's ma last word. Now, aet yer fish."

**L**ATER that evening, when Aggie had gone off to the Rural, Sammy and Walter were left sitting at home watching TV. It was a fairly poor sitcom involving the usual interminable yatter from English middle-class suburbia. Neither Dreep found it particularly riveting.

"I widna worry aboot yer mither," said Walter presently. "She'll come roon."

"Ye ken fine there's nae hope o' that," said Sammy. "She's thrawn. I can forget the car." He sighed. "I dinna ken why I bothered sittin ma test. Wastit ma time. Wastit ma money."

"Now, now, now," said Walter reproachfully. "There's aye a back road for solvin a problem."

"Lateral thinkin?" said Sammy.

"You've been at the varsity," said Walter.

**T**HEY cooked up a scheme between them to time a particular job interview at Inverurie for early on Friday. They knew that Aggie had a date to visit the Lochnagar Distillery Visitor Centre, in the company of three other chums, all morning.

Timed well, Sammy could nip into the car as soon as his mother disappeared over the horizon, get to Inverurie, have his interview, get home and clean the car before Aggie returned.

He left with his father's heartfelt plea ringing in his ears; be careful with the Escort.

Sammy pulled into Inverurie shortly after 11am, well on time to find the premises, calm his nerves and collect his thoughts. But, unused to driving in a place as large and complex as the capital of the Garioch, Sammy began to get a little flustered.

When he had driven round Market Place for the fourth time, he decided he was lost. Panic perspiration began to appear on his brow. He glanced at his watch. Eleven twenty. Just ten minutes left. He'd be late. No excuse. Another chance of a job gone.

A car tooted at him for a particularly careless manoeuvre and he cursed himself. He shot through a pedestrian crossing and alarmed a pensioner with her bag of messages. She shook her fist at him, but Sammy's mind was elsewhere.

Eventually, deciding that he had to break out of the endless round of roads, he chanced going down a narrow, single-track street.

A one-way street.

And he was going the wrong way.

He would have got away with it had not a large and particularly unfriendly bobby been patrolling along the pavement; a prominent example of community policing at its best.

The bobby stepped out into the street and held up his hand. Sammy, now wide-eyed with panic, jabbed at the brakes. The tyres gave a little screech and a little puff of blue rubber-smoke.

The bobby strolled — almost sauntered — up to the passsenger window.

Sammy stared at the dashboard and then, almost blindly and unthinkingly, wound down the window slowly.

The bobby looked pointedly at the no-entry sign back at the entrance to the street, as if to convey the seriousness of the crime.

Then he coughed and, looming over the driver's side of the car, said in his best imposing voice.

"I suppose you know why I have stopped you, sir?"

"Yes," said Sammy in a very small voice.

"And why would that be, sir?" said the bobby.

"Because," said Sammy. "This car's nae insured for me and the MoT ran oot last month."

# Reading of the will

*Episodes 209 and 210 : October 12 and 19, 1991*

WHEN he put the phone down, Walter Dreep stood still in the lobby and tried to collect his thoughts. It hadn't been so much a surprise; more a shock. He was still standing there, motionless, when Aggie bustled out of the front room, carrying her knitting basket. She stumbled to a halt when she saw him.

"Michty, Walter, ye've nae took a turn, hiv ye?" she inquired.

"The phone," stammered Walter. "I got a phone call. I've come in for a windfall. Something that's til ma advantage, the boy said."

"Siller?" said Aggie.

"Could be," said Walter. "The boy didna say. He jist said: 'Be at Rothienorman next Tuesday morning at 11am when you will learn something to your advantage.' "

Aggie put down her knitting on the lobby chair and bored in about her husband. "That's siller, that, Walter," she said, almost whispering. "Solicitor boys dinna use words lik that unless there's money on the go. Far aboot at Rothienorman?"

"Rob and Mysie Gype's hoose," said Walter. "There's a readin o' the will."

"Rob Gype?" she said. "He hidna twa maiks for rubbin thegither. Readin his will winna tak lang."

"Ye'd be surprised," said Walter. "I aye thocht Rob Gype wis a dark horse. I think he poored a fair bitta cash intil the Stock Market."

"Rob Gype poored a' his cash doon his throat," snapped Aggie. "I widna waste the petrol gaun til Rothienorman."

COME Tuesday morning, Walter was standing in front of the hallstand mirror, straightening the knot in his tie, when Aggie appeared behind him, fluffing up the silk scarf with which she had adorned her neck.

"Ye're affa toffed-up like," observed Walter.

"I'm comin wi ye," said Aggie. "I'm nae haein ye traivellin a' that wye yersel."

Walter smiled and reached for his coat.

There was a long line of cars outside the Gypes' cottar hoosie at the back of Rothienorman. Walter drove in at the end of the queue, got out and waited for Aggie to join him before they strode up the road to the gate.

It was a crisp autumn day. There was a mistiness in the air that caught the breath and sharpened the senses. At the garden gate, they bumped into another couple whose faces they recognised vaguely. They half-nodded an acknowledgement and followed them up the path, wondering who they were.

Inside, the house was packed. Thirty or 40 folk were crammed into the sitting-room and parlour. They were of varying shapes and sizes, all with the ruddy complexion of farming folk and all sporting their Sunday-best.

Most of the chaps had added several inches to their waists since their suits had been bought, and the rather ill-fitting assembly looked mildly comical. Low ceilings accentuated the buzz.

Walter and Aggie nodded and smiled exaggerated smiles across the front room at one or two long-time friends and then found a spot against the far wall, where they stood with a couple they knew vaguely from Auchterless.

"An affa steer," observed the man, and Walter and Aggie nodded.

"Nae seats or nithing," said the wife. "Ye'd think they'd mak sure they'd enough seats afore they invitit crowds lik this. I'm nae weel enough for stannin. My doctor telt me that. My various veins is playin up. Mind you, Robbie Gype nivver hid nae consideration for ither fowk."

"An ill-trickit devil," said the man. "I widna bet that a' this palaver isna a joke, ye ken. He's probably up there lookin doon — or doon there lookin up — lachin lik a midden drain at a'b'dy packit in here. Ill-trickit's fit Rob wis."

"Did ye get a phone call?" ventured Walter.

"A wikk past Monday," confirmed the man. "Something til ma advantage, the boy said. Well, ye dinna like insultin the boy fan he's been til a' that trouble phonin. So we jist thocht we'd tak a runnie by."

"Oota respect, like," said the wife.

And Walter and Aggie nodded. An awkward silence fell about them for a few moments, then the man asked: "Div ye ken the form?"

Walter and Aggie looked blank.

"I mean," said the man, "hiv ye been at a will afore?"

Walter and Aggie shook their heads. "Nae really," said Aggie. "I've been at a christenin in a front room, bit that's nae really the same, is it?"

"The last readin we wis at wis a real comedy," said the man. "It wis obvious the deceased couldna abide his brither-in-law. Well, I couldna hiv blamed him, really. The brither-in-law wis a real holy wullie. Jist a richt killjoy. Well, the deceased's man o' business wis readin oot the bequests. A car til the dother; the fairm til the loon; siller til the wife. . ."

". . .then he comes til the brither-in-law," said the wife.

The husband looked sharply at his spouse. "Excuse me, Elsie," he said. "Bit this is my story, this. Div ye mind?"

The wife bristled slightly, but retreated. The husband harumphed and carried on. "Onywye," he said, "the solicitor boy wis readin oot a' this will, then he comes til the brither-in-law. Ye could nearly see the greed shining in the boy's face.

" 'Finally,' said the solicitor, 'I come to the deceased's brother-in-law, Herbert. In the deceased's words: "To my brother-in-law, who kept on telling me that health is better than wealth, I leave..." ' "

And the husband paused for dramatic effect.

" '. . . twa Disprin.' "

IT TOOK another 20 minutes of animated conversation before the lawyer drew everyone to attention. A small, bespectacled man, he sat in the middle of a sofa which had seen better days, having borne the brunt of several generations of fairm chiels and dogs.

In a long preamble, which hushed the crowd not because it was interesting but because no one wanted to miss the good stuff coming later, he announced that Mr Robbie Gype had made provision in his will for his family. He went into several minutes of details.

Mr Gype, he said, had also left £100 in premium bonds to the nurse at Peterhead Cottage Hospital who had tended his broken leg in 1936 after he had been kicked round a park by an ill-tempered bull.

Walter turned to the man standing next to him. "Robbie wis fee'd at Boddam, of coorse," he whispered, and the man nodded, trying at the same time to be sure he wasn't missing anything.

"That must hiv been an affa accident, that," whispered Walter again.

"I dinna think it wis an accident," hissed the man. "I think the bull really meant it."

The guests were beginning to get fidgety, and the air was becoming just a little stuffy and muggy, when the solicitor cleared his throat, as if preparing for a major announcement.

"Now," he said, "Mr Gype was conscious of the debt he owed to his many, many friends down the years. Their support and goodwill were assets he valued highly.

He has fond memories of his upbringing at Auchterless, his time as a farm apprentice at Boddam, the early days of his marriage at Stronach, and finally the full blossoming of his career at Dubbybogs of Rothie, where he attained the not inconsiderable rank of grieve.

There were buzzes and mumbles from the audience. Some of the older billies took the chance to cough a few ripe, hoasty coughs, and the solicitor looked over the rim of his spectacles before he deemed a suitable silence had fallen again.

"To name these individual friends and colleagues over such a long career would take much longer than we have time for here this morning," said the lawyer.

"However, Mr Gype felt particularly attached to Edna and Billy Goloch, from Boddam, and Peter and Jean Hunker, from Auchterless.

Various people in the assembly tried looking discreetly to see how the Golochs' and Hunkers' spirits must have risen.

"However," said the lawyer, "the aforementioned couples have found themselves unable to attend today, and will be made aware of the contents of their bequests as soon as is practicable.

The assembly turned its attention back to the lawyer.

"It was Mr Gype's intention that he should reward his many acquaintances over the years in a style which reflected their generous outlook and their charity towards himself and his family members.

"It is commonly known that Mr Gype found himself often in dire financial straits, and that his impoverished circumstances led him many a time and oft to call on the generosity of others — many of you here present."

Men and women around the assembly were already trying hard to recall examples of their supposed generosity towards the Gype family — but could recall only telling Rob to get lost.

"Many were unable to help," continued the lawyer, "assuring Mr Gype that their financial circumstances were similarly straitened, and offered the considered advice that if he were not so enthusiastic a patron of the local hostelries, his financial position might be more sound."

The puzzled silence now lay heavily. The coughing had stopped. The fidgeting had gone.

"Mr Gype was aware that, at the time, he might have reacted adversely on occasion to such well-meant and constructive advice. He wishes me to convey to you all his bitter regrets at such reaction and behaviour. It was unseemly and ill-considered. He wishes me to inform you that, genuinely, he wished you well in your subsequent purchases of new cookers, cars and holidays abroad.

"Frequently, he felt, only the promise of a bequest on his death touched the hearts of acquaintances sufficiently to allow them to alleviate his financial embarrassment."

"That's richt enough," hissed Aggie to Walter. "Robbie Gype wis aye sayin: 'I'll gie ye a mention in ma will if ye gie's a a coupla poun ivnoo.' "

"And so," said the lawyer, "it was his earnest wish, in his last will and testament, that I gather together as many of his friends, acquaintances, counsellors and advisers in his family's sorrow so that he might fulfil his promise. Whatever else Mr Gype might have been, he was an honourable man."

The lawyer cleared his throat, adjusted his glasses and began reading:

"And so, to all of you here present, Mr Gype's own text reads:

" 'To all of you, my good friends from Auchterless, Boddam, Stronach and Rothie; who stood by me — and watched — over the years, and to everyone I promised would get a mention in my will, here it is . . .

" 'Hello, a'b'dy.'. "

# A colonel calls

*Episode 214 : November 16, 1991*

HAVING recuperated successfully from his minor heart attack at the beginning of August, Erchie Sotter was soon reinstalled on his stool at the Stronach Arms lounge bar. Traditionally, the last stool at the far end of the bar, next to the display case of Havana cigars, has always been Erchie's.

Five or six years ago, the regulars clubbed together and bought a little wooden sign bearing the legend *Erchie's Perchie*, which they hung with great ceremony above the stool.

During his enforced vacancy this summer, regulars respectfully avoided occupying the seat, and it stood vacant even at the busiest times. Strangers who seemed as if they might be casting covetous eyes at Erchie's Perchie were kindly urged to find alternative seating. The barman brooked no argument.

On Erchie's return, he was treated to a half of lager shandy and a nip on the house, which he downed promptly, smacked his lips and beamed to the assembly.

He pushed the two glasses back across the bar to the barman and looked up expectantly — but none was forthcoming. His welcome back seemed to have expired rather more rapidly than he would have liked.

For the first few weeks, one or two softer-hearted villagers would relent and buy him a welcome-back drink. Soon, even those faded away and Erchie was left once more to fund his own liquid refreshment.

Only when a stranger turned up in the bar was Erchie able to practise his mooching skills. Even then, his success rate seemed to be diminishing; a fact which he put down to the recession.

"There's nae as muckle disposable income aboot nooadays," he said knowledgeably to John the Barman one evening. "I read that in the Press and Journal personal-finance bittie, so it maun be richt enough. Nae disposable income."

"Well, Erchie," said John, idly drying a glass. "There's naeb'dy saft enough to dispose o' their income doon your throat, onywye."

"Ye're mebbe richt there," sighed Erchie. "It's a hard world turned. A selfish world." And he gazed sadly at the bartop for a few moments. John thought briefly about how the fire had gone out of Erchie since his spell in hospital.

At that, the outside door flew open, the November chill blew in around the bar and a heavy-set gentleman in his late sixties or early seventies, stamped in.

He shut the door behind him and the roar of the wintry blast receded. He stamped his feet once or twice more, slipped off his camelhair coat, slung it over his arm, then approached the bar, smoothing down the windblown tufts of hair at the back of his head.

"A pint of your very best brew, landlord," he said in the plummy tones of a Sandhurst military man. "And I'll trouble you for a hot rum punch as a chaser, if I may."

"The only thing het roon here's the bradies," said the barman.

"And even they're nae affa het," chipped in Erchie.

"Goodness me," mused the stranger, "this really *is* the back end of the civilised world, isn't it?" He brightened almost at once, however, and slapped a cheery hand on the bar. "In that case, I shall forgo the punch in favour of your local brew. Be quick about you, my man, and look lively."

Defiantly slowly, and mustering as withering a look as he could manage, John moved off to the taps, leaving Erchie and the stranger side by side.

"Erchibald Sotter," said Erchie, offering his outstretched hand of welcome to the portly stranger.

"Colonel Aloysius St John Whitsun-Smythe," said the stranger brightly. He reached into his inside pocket for a comb, which he began stroking carefully through his ample handlebar moustache.

"I'm a stranger in these parts," he said, still combing. "But, dash it, I've been a stranger in most parts almost all my days."

"Really?" said Erchie, shifting on his stool so he faced the man more squarely, "and how's that?"

"Wandering spirit, I suppose," said the colonel. "Military man, you know. Career military. Sandhurst. Up and at em, and all that sort of thing. Jerry. Korea, Fuzzies, Mau-Mau. Yes, I've seen action in lots of theatres."

"I wis mair a back-seats-at-the-pictures man, masel," said Erchie. "Plenty action there, though."

Stuck for a moment, and evidently unimpressed, the colonel cleared his throat. He stood patiently for a few moments but, deciding that the barman was apparently going to be a little longer than he hoped, felt forced to carry on the conversation with Erchie.

"And yourself?" he said. "Military man?"

"Train driver, retired," said Erchie. "And I aye found ye developed a terrible thirst drivin a train. A' that smoke, I suppose."

The colonel, however, seemed oblivious to the hint, so Erchie was forced to continue.

"Bein a train man, *I'm* a bit o' a wanderin spirit, as weel," he said. "Stronach til Aiberdeen, Aiberdeen til Stronach, back and fore, back and fore, ilky day for thirty year. Then Beeching shut ma line. I wis near by masel wi grief, I needed a gweed stiff drink that day, I can tell ye."

"Beeching, what a blighter," said the colonel empathetically. "Dashed fine

71

trains in Kenya, though. British-built, you know. Africa? Has the best of everything. Take it from me. I know. I've been there. Did I say? During the Mau-Mau. Nasty business. Nasty business."

"Nesty business, bit rare trains, eh?" said Erchie.

"What?" said the colonel. "Oh, yes. Marvellous trains. Absolute corkers. Great big steamy brutes. Those African johnnies didn't know when they were well-off. Dancing up and down in their loin-cloths till we British took them by the scruff of the neck. Gratitude? Gratitude my behind."

"I suppose the Mau-Mau werena great drinkers," said Erchie, "nae the sorta fowk ye could buy a friendly drink for."

John slid the pint of heavy towards the colonel, who offered a fiver in return. He took his first sip as eagerly as if he had been stuck in the Sahara for a fortnight.

"Nectar," he said lyrically. "A fine brew, that, landlord." But John said nothing and simply shoved the colonel's change back across the counter.

"Now," said the colonel, returning to Erchie, "what more can I tell you about myself?"

"Ye were tellin me how ye bocht drinks in Kenya," said Erchie.

"Was I?" said the colonel. "You wouldn't want to drink the local brew in Kenya. Dreadful stuff. Dreadful. You could strip doors with it, you know."

"Ye're a DIY man, are ye?" said Erchie, searching for a more fruitful vein of conversation. "Thirsty work, DIY."

"What?" said the colonel. "Oh, no, not at all. Couldn't tell you the difference between a saw and a hammer. Hopeless. Totally hopeless. No, I'm more your outdoors type. That was one good thing about East Africa; every other day, out in the Serengeti, blasting the living daylights out of anything that moved. Those were the days. Hunting and shooting."

He gazed wistfully into the middle distance, as if overcome with nostalgia. Then he came to himself once again. "Of course, having been a train-driver, you won't be very familiar with hunting and shooting, eh?"

"Mebbe no," said Erchie, finally admitting defeat, slipping off his stool and preparing to head for the door, "though I wis sharp enough on shuntin and hootin."

# Mother Dreep: VIP

*Episode 220 : December 24, 1991*

I T IS A TRADITION of Stronach that the minister pays a call on the oldest woman of the parish on the day before Christmas Eve and the oldest man of the parish on the day before Hogmanay. Since the unfortunate demise of old Widow Blate in July, the mantle of oldest woman had fallen on the shoulders of Walter Dreep's mother.

Unfortunately, Mother Dreep has been confined to her bed in the front room at Walter and Aggie's house for a few days. A chill and stomach pains have laid her low. Despite her North-east phlegm and determination, she has had to admit defeat and let the ailments run their course. She was duly confined to quarters while Walter scurried about, alternately running errands for her and for Aggie.

Walter had called the doctor to ask for a home visit and the doctor had promised as full and extensive an examination as a home visit would allow. The prospect had not pleased Mother Dreep.

"Ye ken fine I dinna like that new doctor," she barked at her son when he told her the news. "Him and his caul hands. I'm an aul wifie, Walter. I've still ma pride."

"Better that ye get roadit, though, mither," said Walter cheerfully as he picked up her tray of tea things on Sunday night. "So that's an end till't. Onywye, ye've the minister comin the morn wi a bokie o' flooers for ye, you bein the aulest wifie in the parish noo. Ye canna be less than yer best, fit wi you bein a VIP."

M OTHER Dreep had a restless night. She had tossed and turned as much as her rheumatics and three ridiculously fluffy pillows allowed. She finally nodded off shortly after 5am, and it was at 7am that Walter burst in with a cup of tea, a digestive biscuit and her teeth in an old jam jar.

"Come on, mither," said Walter, laying down the cup, plate and jar and reaching up to throw back the curtains. "My wird," he said, almost as if he had been surprised. "My wird, it's a black mornin."

"It's still dark," muttered Mother Dreep from the depths of her pillows. She had sunk so far in that only her nose was showing. Walter stepped across and slipped his arms behind her back to hoist her up.

She didn't like it. "Watch fit ye're grabbin," she wailed. "Lord, ye're roch. I'm an aul wifie and ye're heistin me up lik a bagga tatties."

"Come on, mither," said Walter, blithely ignoring his mother's protestations. "Ye ken ye've the minister and the doctor comin the day. Ye canna lie there stinkin a' mornin."

"I'll lie here as lang's I please," said Mother Dreep, taking her tea and dunking her digestive. "If they canna tak me as they find me, that's their lookoot." She sucked fondly on the wet digestive, then stopped, as if struck by a thought.

"It's nae that new minister, is't?"

"It is," said Walter. "Mr Thole. A fine mannie."

"I dinna like a new minister," said Mother Dreep. "Ye tak a while or ye get intil the set o' a new minister. I likit wir aul minister. He'd a couthy wye aboot him. I wis used til him. It wis him that mairriet me and yer faither. Can I nae hae ma aul minister peyin me a visit?"

"That minister deed in 1964, mither," said Walter.

"Dash it," said Mother Dreep disgusted. "I thocht I hidna seen him aboot for a file." And she mused for a while about the passing of such an old acquaintance.

"Aye, weel," she said, snapping out of her reverie. He's earned his rest up the golden staircase, richt enough. Man, he wis a richt gweed minister, though. Een o' the aul school. A richt fire-and-brimstone, minister, him, and nae mistake. Ye kent far ye were wi that minister. He telt ye straicht."

"Aye, mither," said Walter, searching for his mother's slippers and only half-listening to what she was saying.

"Aye," she said, warming to her theme. "Ministers wisna jist ministers in my day. They wis leaders o' the community, and we wis a lot the better for't. We hidna naewye near the crime and coorseness we hiv nooadays. Nivver nott yer social workers and wheens o' bobbies traivellin roon and roon aboot in circles in their little carries. Ministers kent the secret. Richt gweed ministers. Thunderin fae the pulpit aboot eternal damnation and sins o' the flesh."

"Aye, mither," said Walter, "that wid fairly pit a body aff, that, richt enough. A' that thunderin fae the pulpit. A' that sins o' the flesh."

"Of coorse it put folk aff," snapped Mother Dreep. "Folk kent better. Folk hid standards in my young day. The dominies educatit yer mind. The ministers educatit yer soul."

She lay back gently into her pillows, as if overtaxed, and purred fondly: "I nivver kent aboot sins o' the flesh til I met the minister."

She lay there, smiling fondly, while Walter fussed about looking for her slippers. It was she who broke the silence a few moments later.

"A new doctor. A new minister," she whined. "Nithing bides the same nooadays. A'thing changes. Ye nivver ken far ye are wi nithing. It's affa unsettlin, this. Gaun they were onything like the thing, they wid save a' the changes til a' the aul folk wis deid."

74

"Aye, mither," said Walter, sliding her slippers down by her bedside. "Now, are ye gettin up, or will I get Aggie and the pail fae the back porch?"

"I'll see if I can get up," said Mother Dreep. "That tin pail maks an affa racket."

BY 10.30, Mother Dreep had been fed, watered, abluted, adorned and was deemed presentable enough to face her visitors. "Ye hinna phoned the Press and Journal, hiv ye?" she asked hopefully as Walter smoothed down the candlewick bedspread. "They're nae sendin oot a photiegrapher, are they?"

"No," said Walter. "We tried, bit they're coverin a best-decoratit plum-duff competition at Drumoak instead."

"Good Lord," muttered Mother Dreep. "Upstaged by a plum duff."

At that, the doorbell pinged and Walter headed for the bedroom door. "I'll jist send him in," he said.

Walter opened the front door to be faced with the smiling figure of the young doctor. "Hullo, doctor," said Walter. "Ye'll be here for ma mither's examination. She's ben in the front room. It's mair private in there and I suppose ye need privacy wi private things lik an examination."

"Indeed, indeed," said the doctor, stepping inside and waiting to be shown which front room to enter.

"I winna come in, doctor," said Walter. "Nae wi it bein a private examination. In ye go, though. She's waitin for ye." The doctor stepped inside and closed the door behind him. Walter headed through to the scullery.

Three-quarters of an hour later, there was a knock on the scullery door. Walter jumped up from the kitchen table and was half-way to the door when it opened and the doctor announced that he was leaving and that, really, there was nothing to worry about.

"She's ninety-three," he said. "She's remarkable for her years. Plenty of bed rest should do the trick. "I'll give you this prescription for tablets to ease the stomach acid a bit and she'll soon be hunky-dory."

"OK, doctor," said Walter as they walked back along the lobby. His voice dropped to a whisper. "Thank you for comin oot."

"Not at all," said the doctor, opening the front door for himself and stepping outside. "Sometimes a full body examination is the only way to set a patient's mind at rest. Anyway, good day to you."

They shook hands. The doctor strode down the garden path towards his Volvo estate and Walter closed the door.

"Is that the minister awa?" shouted Mother Dreep.

Walter stepped to the side and opened his mother's bedroom door. "That wisna the minister, mother," he said. "That wis the doctor, in deein yer examination."

"Well, that explains that," said Mother Dreep. "I *thocht* he wis affa familiar for a minister."

# Store Wars

**E**BENEZER Grip turned the CLOSED sign to OPEN, yawned and peered out into the blackness of a December morning. He fancied that winters in the vale were becoming longer and colder with every passing year and wondered if now was the time to give up shopkeeping.

He turned and looked round at the interior of the Emporium. It had seen better days, he knew, but people at Stronach didn't care much for new-fangled ways of doing their messages. No self-service supermarkets for them. They preferred the personal touch, and Ebenezer knew it. Besides, how many of them had cars to go haring all the way to Aberdeen for a monthly shop costing £100 and more? Were they not perfectly content with the convenience of something on their own doorstep? Of course they were.

He wandered back towards the counter, walked through the gap and pulled down the flap behind himself. He reached for the power point on the far wall beside the cigarette shelves and switched it on to fire up the electric cash register, his sole concession to modern technology, although he hated it with a passion. He would dearly have preferred to carry on with the old piano-key model which had been such a trusty servant for so many years.

The little green lights glowed and the register rattled and hummed and whined as it sang into life

"Dampt thing," he muttered. "Jist wastin electric."

He bent under the counter for a duster and swiped it idly over the surface. He had dusted the counter only the night before, and there was no cleaner counter in the whole of North-east Scotland, but he was a traditional shopkeeper; a creature of habit, and if his trade was worth calling a trade at all, it was worth doing well, to acceptable standards.

He turned and flicked the duster at a few 14oz cans of baked beans, but they, too, had been spotless and he was simply following a ritual; the same sort of ritual that would see Erchie Sotter walking through the Emporium front door at 6.47am precisely, with his copy of that day's Press and Journal; hoisting himself on to the stool which Ebenezer always kept beside the counter for his frailer customers, or for those who liked to stop for a rest and a news, and chatting about plans for the day.

It was a bit pointless, chatting about plans for the day, thought Ebenezer, for every day was very much the same as the one before it, and certainly the same as the one which would follow it. Things were like that if you were a shopkeeper. Monotonous routine was just one of those sacrifices one had to endure when one had dedicated one's life to serving the public. At least, that was Ebenezer's reasoning and he felt comfortable with it.

He looked up at the old clock he had bought when the village railway station had closed in 1965. It ticked steadily, sensibly and inexorably towards 6.47. As the minute hand moved over the XII, the bell on the door pinged and in out of the blackness came Erchie, stamping his feet for warmth and carrying his rolled-up P&J under his oxter.

"Erchie," said Ebenezer, by way of acknowledgement as Erchie hoisted himself on to the stool.

"Ebenezer," said Erchie, returning the gesture, and he opened out his paper and began scanning the sports pages. "Aiberdeen nae deein affa weel ivnoo," he said. "This maun be the worst Aiberdeen team since the war, ye ken that? They couldna play their wye oot o' a paper bug. They couldna save their breath. They couldna pass win'." He flicked agitatedly on to the front page, where news of another rise in interest rates was the Page One lead story. "Mair bad news," he said. He scanned the rest of the front page, had a wee smile to himself at the cartoon, and turned inside. "I suppose ye'll be needin a fly cup," said Ebenezer, turning and heading for the back shop.

"Jist if ye're makkin," said Erchie from behind his newspaper, and Ebenezer walked through to the sink in the back shop. He was standing filling the kettle at the old brass tap when he heard Erchie shout: "Michty! Ebenezer! Fit aboot this?"

Ebenezer finished filling the kettle calmly, for he knew Erchie's excitements of old, and this one would likely turn out as all the others — a sore anticlimax. He wandered through to the front shop. "Aye?" he said.

"Listen til this," said Erchie, and he folded open his paper at Page Three. "*Village Hits the Shopping Big Time. Two Glasgow entrepreneur brothers who made their fortune by setting up a new generation of village shops throughout the Central Belt have turned their eyes to the North-east. They have selected Stronach as the site for their first venture north of Stirling and are confident that their new premises can be up and running inside a year.*"

Erchie looked up at Ebenezer, who had paled visibly and had slumped on to the stool at his side of the counter. Erchie carried on reading.

"*The brothers, Soon Fat Lo and Soon Ping Lee, who are of Chinese descent, head a multi-million-pound trading company which turned over £45million last year on the strength of a network of 127 village shops in Strathclyde, Lothian and Central regions. The brothers attribute their astonishing success to precise marketing and low pricing.*"

Ebenezer whimpered quietly.

"*The brothers are convinced that the North-east of Scotland is ripe for a new generation of discount shops in all small villages and are keen to take on the might of the national superstore chains. 'We have proved in the Central Belt that we can give the big boys a bloody nose,' said Soon Fat Lo at his Glasgow HQ yesterday. 'We think the time has come to look farther afield to bring the benefits of our deep discounting to a new clientele in the North-east of Scotland. We have chosen the small village of Stronach as a site where there is no appreciable shopping service at the moment and where we know we can be off to a flying start.' The Soon Brothers' store is expected to be trading by October next year.*"

Erchie let the paper fall to his knees and looked up at Ebenezer, but Ebenezer was holding his head in his hands, rocking back and forth on the stool gently and whimpering softly to himself. Erchie slipped off his stool and stepped towards the counter.

"Michty, Ebenezer," he said. "The big boys is comin for yer trade. It sounds a bittie like the Ark Royal squarin up til a boatie on the pleasure-park pond. I think ye could be goosed. Ye could be bankrupt this time next year. The Emporium could be finished. Doon the tubes. Up the swannee."

Ebenezer looked up. If it were possible for a 94-year-old man to have aged 40 years, Ebenezer looked as if he had managed it. "Thanks, Erchie," he said. "Thanks for yer support in ma time o' crisis."

BEFORE 9am that day, virtually the whole of Stronach was a-buzz with the news. Unlike Ebenezer, they were not at all despondent at the prospect of incomers setting up in competition to the Emporium. On the contrary, there was jubilation in almost every household as they reached Page Three of their paper. Several villagers were already planning the holidays they would have with the vast amounts of money they would be saving on groceries.

One or two were sufficiently unfeeling to trot round to the Emporium with the paper still warm in their hands to inquire if Ebenezer was at all worried by what lay ahead. "Nae really," Ebenezer would say, trying his best to put a brave face on a very dark situation. "The Emporium's been here far langer nor you and me put thegither, and she'll fairly haud oot against onything that twa brithers fae Glasgow can fling at her. Dinna you fash yersel."

"Oh, *we're* nae worried, Ebenezer," they would say, sauntering from the shop and smirking. "We jist thocht you'd maybe be a bittie concerned aboot the competition."

"Healthy stuff, competition," he would say, and the door would shut and he would hear muffled laughing as his customers trotted off down the street.

That night, after close of business, he made himself a cup of tea as usual and sat down on his own at the old wooden table in the back shop where his father had taught him the rudiments of the business all those years before. He looked up at the shelves of stock; at cases of cat food and Ovaltine and butter and baked beans.

He was looking at his life.

He was looking at a 65-year career.

And he couldn't help wondering if he was looking at the end of it all.

He thought for a few minutes more then he pushed back his chair, stood up and walked towards the old safe on the floor in the corner. He twisted the combination, hauled open the cast-iron door and peered inside for his ledgers.

That night, Ebenezer didn't go to bed. He sat at the old wooden table, ledgers spread before him, wondering how he, a small shopkeeper, could put up an effective fight against such an aggressive competitor.

By the time the old station clock struck five, he knew that he couldn't. He could keep it going for a few months perhaps; maybe even a year, but the outcome was inevitable. He could go on fighting, or he could do the sensible thing and shut up shop before he lost all his savings. He was 94, after all. He had given it a good go. He had made a steady, if unspectacular, living. He had earned his rest.

The Emporium would have to close for good.

He leaned back in his seat, looked round the back shop once more and then, quite quickly, he fell asleep.

**E**BENEZER was still sleeping almost two hours later when Erchie turned up at the front door of the shop, wondering why the place was still locked up. Erchie hammered on the door for a good two minutes, becoming increasingly concerned that he was getting no response. He wandered round to the side door and battered on that for another minute. Still nothing.

Erchie was wondering how long it would take him to run down to the police station when he heard the bolt slide back on the front door and he trotted round to the front to find Ebenezer, yawning and rubbing his eyes, lifting the blind and turning round the sign to OPEN.

Erchie walked in as soon as Ebenezer pulled open the door. "Michty, Ebenezer," he said, "ye'd me really worried there for a minute. That must be the first time in sixty-five year that ye've missed half-past six."

"I suppose so," said Ebenezer, shutting the door. "Are ye for yer cuppie?"

"I'll mak the cuppie this mornin," said Erchie. "Here; you sit doon and read the paper," and he whipped his Press and Journal from under his oxter and thrust it at Ebenezer.

But when Erchie came back five minutes later bearing two steaming mugs of tea, Ebenezer hadn't even opened the paper. He was slumped in the seat at a most awkward angle, snoring softly. The man was absolutely shattered. Erchie walked him through to the back sitting-room, laid him out on the sofa and covered him up with the tartan travelling-rug which lay draped across the back. Erchie decided that he would be playing shopkeeper that day.

**E**BENEZER didn't wake until almost seven that evening, by which time Erchie had nearly completed a reasonably healthy day's trading. When Ebenezer shambled through to see what was happening, he discovered Erchie dusting down the counter and almost on the point of switching off one bar of the electric heater above the door.

"Ye hinna hid twa bars goin on that heater a' day, hiv ye?" said Ebenezer.

"Yes, I hiv," said Erchie. "I'm nae freezin til death for naebody. Nae even you, ye aul goat. Sit doon there or I get ye a cuppie." And Ebenezer, obediently, did as he was told while Erchie passed him en route to the kettle in the back shop.

Five minutes later, the two of them were sitting down, tea in hand, but not speaking. Erchie studied Ebenezer, who was looking sadly into his tea.

81

"It'll maybe nivver happen," said Erchie at last, and Ebenezer looked up.

"Of coorse it'll happen," he said. "Nae businessman announces his plans in public if he's nae certain that they'll happen. You mark my words, that boys'll be openin up their shop here bang on schedule at the hinder end o' next year. And that's the date I'll be shuttin up the Emporium."

"Ye're nae closin doon?" said Erchie, aghast, slipping off the stool.

"I've nae option," said Ebenezer. "I'd be cuttin ma throat if I didna."

"Ye canna shut," said Erchie. "Folk depends on ye. Ye're the village shop Ye're an institution."

"Nae efter next winter," said Ebenezer. "Hoo Flung Dung. They'll be the institutions hereaboots fae next November. And there's nithing I can dee that'll stop it."

"Folk winna desert ye," said Erchie. "They winna use this new shop. Folk sticks wi fit they ken. They'll be loyal til ye. Look at the service they've gotten fae ye this last sixty-five year. They canna jist ignore that. They canna be that callous."

"Can they nae?" said Ebenezer wisely. "If you thocht ye wid get yer messages twinty per cent cheaper roon the corner, wid you nae shop there? Or wid you stick wi the same aul place far ye usually dee yer messages? A place that's been needin modernisin for the best part o' thirty year. A place that's past its glory days. A placie that's needin its rest. And an aul shopkeeper that's gotten tired o' keepin goin."

Erchie was horrified. "This is nae Ebenezer spikkin," he said. "Nae Ebenezer Grip. World War One flyin ace. Nae the man that nivver shirked a battle."

"I'm shirkin noo," said Ebenezer. "Will you shut up the shop? I'm awa til ma bed."

And Ebenezer slid off the stool and shambled past Erchie into the back shop.

That was when Erchie determined to find a way out of this stickiest of sticky situations.

OVER succeeding weeks, Ebenezer's mood deteriorated noticeably. More and more, Erchie had to draft himself in to keep the Emporium and General Stores going when Ebenezer couldn't be bothered. Erchie took it upon himself to order the stock. He tended to the customers, dealt with travellers and did the cleaning. He even took it upon himself to lose that day's Press and Journal if the paper contained any further news about the Soon Brothers' plans.

By February, the whole village knew in great detail the incomers' business intentions and how Stronach would be the springboard for a great new retail empire throughout the North and North-east of Scotland. They knew how bulk buying and restricted stock would give them price reductions bettering even the big superstores in Aberdeen and, quite frankly, most of Stronach could not wait for the store to begin trading.

Most of Stronach except Erchie, that was. He had noticed how quickly his old friend had declined in spirit and he knew that he didn't have much time left. Every day brought worse and worse news in the paper. The Soon Brothers had revised their estimates of sales upwards and considered that they could cut their prices by another 5% over and above their original estimates. They had been given permission to revise the floorspace of their store from 4,500sq.ft to 6,200sq.ft on the strength of market research.

Worst of all, at the end of February, the Press and Journal had carried an interview with the older Soon brother and had given him a fairly hard time about invading a small village and siphoning off all the profits Down South, whereas the current system in small villages ensured that all the money was kept locally.

Mr Soon had thought about this deeply and, off the cuff, had told the reporter that he would buy all his fresh produce locally, instead of shipping it up from the Central Belt suppliers he favoured. As a result, he said, growers and farmers and service-providers throughout the Howe of Stronach could also cash in on the boom to come. Now what was there to complain of?

Erchie could not believe what he was reading. It was getting 10 times worse. He dared not let Ebenezer even glance at the paper. And as he carried on reading, he found the Soon Brothers guaranteeing much more adventurous produce lines. For once, small villages could sample some of the exotic flavours and tastes and foods that only big-city delicatessens and national superstore chains could offer. He would be opening whole new shopping vistas for the people of Stronach and, soon, for small villages everywhere.

And so keen were the Soon Brothers to meet their new customers that they would be visiting Stronach on the Friday, accompanying a market-research team flown in especially from London to make final checks on likely sales volume and customer attitudes.

That was when Erchie's plan began to take shape.

THE Soon Brothers' Bentley hushed into the bottom end of Stronach shortly after 9.30am on the Friday. Already, a goodly proportion of the village was out to see it, or was craning its collective neck behind the net curtains to catch a glimpse of the village's new benefactors and retail gurus.

The Bentley came to a halt beside the fountain in the village square, and two little men in camel-hair coats stepped from the back. They stopped and sniffed the sharp March air. Across beside the phone box, a muffled clapping got up, but Babbie Girn gave Dorothy Birze a sharp powk on the shoulder to behave herself and the clapping stopped.

The two Soons smiled at each other and stepped towards Dorothy and Babbie. They stopped in front of the two women and bowed slightly.

"We are very pleased to meet you," said the taller man in a very crisp English accent. It is good to know that we are among friends."

"Is it true yer baked beans'll be nine pee a can?" inquired Dorothy.

"It is true," said the other brother. "Perhaps even eightpence. Who can tell with the state of the baked-bean market these days?"

"Eicht pee a can," said Dorothy excitedly. "And fit aboot yer cat food?"

"Exceptionally cheap, my dear lady," said the first Soon brother. "What is your name?"

"Mrs Dorothy Mima Birze," said Dorothy. "You can ca' me Dosh."

"Mrs Birze," said the first brother, "on our opening day, you must come and meet me again and remind me of our encounter this morning. I will see to it personally that you receive a case of your favourite cat food with the compliments of my brother and myself. Think of it as a small thank-you for the warmth of your welcome for two strangers on such a cold March morning."

"A hale case?" said Dorothy.

The brothers smiled, bowed again and turned to walk up the street.

"Whiskas wi rubbit chunks?" called Dorothy.

THE brothers spent an inordinate amount of time in the village that morning. They spent only a few minutes at the site earmarked for their shop, for they were confident about their plans in that direction. Instead, they seemed more interested in the village itself and the sort of people who lived there.

They wandered up and down the Main Street, shadowing the market-research teams with their clipboards; listening carefully but discreetly to the enthusiastic answers given when cheaper prices were mentioned and congratulating themselves that they had made another shrewd business move.

"I wonder," said the younger brother to the public-relations consultant they had brought with them, "do you think it would be an appropriate gesture to hold a lunch for the entire village in the local hotel today? I see it as a means of getting to know our future customers — and suppliers — better."

"I don't know if a small hotel could cater for 500 people at such short notice," said the PR man, scanning his clipboard.

"Just something simple," said Mr Soon. "A buffet, perhaps. Nothing elaborate. Just enough to let them think that we care. . . I mean, to let them *see* that we care, of course."

"Of course, Mr Soon," said the PR man. "I will attend to it right away."

"If they are reluctant," said Mr Soon, "tell them that we might put a lot business their way in future. That should clinch the deal. It usually does. If not, you might suggest that a small hotel which cannot do business with a major retail company might be placing inordinate difficulties in its own path for quite a long way into the future."

"I understand, Mr Soon," said the PR man.

But not only the PR man had understood. Standing up the alley beside the post office, Babbie Girn had understood, too.

And she didn't much care for it.

84

NEWS travelled fast that the two brothers had organised a free buffet lunch in the Stronach Arms function suite. Queues began at 11.30am and as soon as the doors opened the swarm of villagers haring for the Scotch broth and bradies surprised even the Soons. When the Grampian Television news crew turned up, the PR man congratulated himself on having secured a tremendous media coup. Now his clients would be portrayed to the whole of the North of Scotland as the munificent benefactors they were. .

The village would be seen welcoming this new breed of retail company; delighted that it was setting up shop in their midst. Soon, every village and small town from Lerwick to Longforgan, from Stornoway to Stonehaven would be begging for the Soons to set up shop in their communities, too. The PR man sniffed a fat bonus.

The Grampian crew plugged in their lights, hoisted the camera and began walking up and down the aisles, framing shots of happy faces slurping at the broth, and interviewing villagers who pronounced the Soon Brothers the greatest retailers since Marks and Spencer.

The TV crew were on their fifth interview when Mr Soon the Elder stood up at the top table on the stage, his camel-hair coat still draped round his shoulders. He clinked a kniife against a wine glass and waited for the buzz to subside.

"Ladies and gentlemen," he said, "it is a great privilege to share with you these moments. I know that we will enjoy a long and fruitful trading relationship and that you will know a tremendous difference in your shopping bills from the end of November this year." A spirited round of applause exploded round the hall. Only Babbie, Erchie, Virginia and Ebenezer remained still.

"As we have our friends from the television company here," continued Mr Soon, "I thought it would be a fine idea for those of you who will be supplying our Stronach store to come up on to the stage and announce your trading agreements with us, just so that the whole community can understand that the Soon Brothers Trading Company appreciates the importance of community support. We want everyone to know that we invest in the communities that we serve. Please come forward."

After a moment's initial reluctance, the farmer from Wester Bogensharn rose from his seat and strode down the side of the hall; his tackety boots echoing with every step. He hauled himself on to the stage, two steps at a time, clasped the microphone, peered against the glare of the TV lights and boomed:

"Fourteen ton o' tatties a wikk. Guaranteed."

He was followed by the owner of the fish farm at Inverspaver. "Four dozen trout and a dozen salmon every day," he announced. "The Soon Brothers will be my biggest single customer and a valued regular order."

The fish-farm manager was followed by a woman from the egg-grading station, a man from the herb garden at Inverspaver, a woman from the apiarist club announcing that she had signed a contract to supply four dozen jars of honey a week. A pig farmer not familiar to anyone announced a contract for 10 bellies of pork every week. A dairy farmer from the bottom end of the Vale of Stronach had signed a contract for several dozen gallons of milk a day.

Soon, a queue had built up at the side of the stage, all suppliers waiting for their turn to anounce their great good fortune in having signed contracts with the Soon Brothers.

Only in the corner at the back was there a sign of dissent. "Bit a' this fowk gaun up on the stage supply me already," said Ebenezer. "There's nae nithing new here. And if this new mob can sell at cheaper prices, they canna be payin the suppliers as much as I div."

"The suppliers are cuttin aff their ain noses and they canna see it," said Virginia.

"And fan they've put you oot o' business, Ebenezer, the Soon Brithers'll whack the prices richt up so we're peyin mair than ivver," said Babbie.

"And ye can bet they winna pit up their payments til the suppliers," said Erchie. "They'll bide their time and then they'll milk this village dry."

"Fit can we dee?" whispered Virginia, as Flo Spurtle appeared at the end of the table with a silver platter of bradies. Erchie reached for a bradie, took a bite, and thought hard. And as he chewed, he had an idea.

He grinned at Babbie, Virginia and Ebenezer, then stood up and strode up to the front of the hall, where the last of the queue of suppliers had reached the microphone. Two minutes later, as everyone was tucking into piles and piles of bradies, Erchie took the microphone from the hand of the previous supplier.

"Ladies and gentlemen," he announced, "I wid jist like til thank Mr Soon and his brither for the contract I've got aff them."

The assembly of 350 stopped in mid-chew of their bradies, wondering what Erchie could be supplying to a supermarket.

"Yes," continued Erchie, turning to face the TV camera. "I am especially delighted to see you all tucking into your bradies this dennertime, because they are the first of the new bradies for which I will be responsible."

Babbie turned to Virginia, but Virginia was just as puzzled.

"Yes, ladies and gentlemen," said Erchie. "I will be collectin a' the squashed hedgehogs and deid cats in the vale for makkin intil these fine bradies. They will also be in a fine range of cold pressed meats. The Soon Brothers are determined that you will enjoy the finest cuisine they have to offer, and they, like me, are delighted to see you horsin intil the bradies like ye are. Tasty, aren't they?"

The rest of Erchie's speech was drowned in a flurry of coughing and spluttering, boos and jeers directed at the platform party. The Soon Brothers were furious, but could do nothing. The TV crew could scarcely keep up with the pandemonium.

Erchie made good his escape from the melee on the stage. The PR man was almost in tears. The Soon Brothers stormed out a side door under a hail of half-eaten bradies and into their Bentley before the TV crew could catch up with them. Across the hall, Virginia, Babbie and Ebenezer were smiling quietly.

"Aye, weel," said Ebenezer, standing up, "I doot that's sortit that oot. And now I maun awa back til the Emporium. A growin business disna rin itsel, ye ken."

# A Taste of Stronach

More marvellous meals
made to make you go
Mmmmmmmmmmmmmmmmm

"There's nithing like a gweed bowlie o' soup on a caul winter's day, is there? Roon yer hert like a hairy worm. Sets ye up for the rest o' the day. And if ye hae it for yer supper it saves yer belly rummlin a' nicht and keepin ye wakkened. I mean hame-made soup, of coorse. I widna hae that tinned stuff in the hoose. I canna understand folk that buys tins o' soup, can you?

Convenience food, they say, bit it's nae ony mair convenient than makkin yer ain, and it's naewye near as fine-tastit. Young quines dinna ken nooadays foo easy hame-made soup really is. There's nae great mystery. It's mair convenience food than ony o' their tins and packets.

Usually, I'm a broth or a tattie-soup wifie. I like it as thick that ye can cut it wi a knife. Bit I'd an affa gweed crop o' carrots this year, so this his been the soup in my kitchen this past whilie. Ma freezer's full o't. Cream o' carrot.

Though I say it masel, I'm real prood o't. It's nae as fillin as tattie, and it's nae as wattery as hame-made tomata. It's an in-atween kinna soup. Try it and see.

# Babbie Girn's
# CREAM OF CARROT SOUP

*(Serves 4-6)*

**Ingredients**
A splash of vegetable oil
1 onion, finely diced
1 leek, sliced finely
450g (1lb) carrots, grated
1.1 litres (2pt) chicken or vegetable stock
Salt and freshly ground pepper
150 ml (¼pint) double cream
Parsley and croutons to garnish

**1.** Heat the oil in a soup pan.

**2.** Soften the onion and the leek in the covered pan for three minutes, then stir in the carrots.

**3.** Add salt and pepper. Cover and cook for another five minutes.

**4.** Add the boiling stock and cover and boil for six minutes. All the vegetables should be cooked .

**5.** Liquidise and return to the rinsed-out pan.

**6.** Reheat and taste for seasoning.

**7.** Off the heat, stir in some of the cream, but remember to reserve some for garnish.

**8.** Ladle the soup into plates. Drizzle the remaining cream over and place the chopped parsley and croutons on the top.

❝I know exactly what you're going to say. You'll say that you can't possibly afford fresh salmon. You're going to say that it might be everyday fare for those affluent, tasteful and frankly stylish Barrington-Grahams up at Bridge House, but that poor humble people like yourselves couldn't possibly aspire to such luxury.

Well, I have to let you into a little secret. This is one of the most economical dishes of all. This recipe serves *ten* people. Far cheaper than smoked salmon, and considerably cheaper than good Aberdeen-Angus beef, And it's just that something different for when you have people round.

One of my previous housekeepers back in Oxfordshire told me all about it. Cecilie was her name. She was Danish, I think. I never spoke to her long enough to find out exactly. Well, it doesn't do to fraternise too much, does it? But they like fish in Denmark, don't they? I discovered that on a weekend break to Copenhagen in May. You simply must ask your fishmonger's advice. He'll be delighted at how adventurous you're being.

# Kate Barrington-Graham's
# GRAVADLAX

900g (2lb) tailpiece of fresh salmon

**Pickling ingredients**

4 tbsps granulated sugar

3 tbsps coarse sea salt

2 tsps whisky **or** 1 tbsp sunflower oil

3 tbsps fresh dill **or** 1 tbsp dried

**Dill and Mustard Sauce**

3 tbsps Dijon Mustard

1 tbsp caster sugar

1 tbsp white-wine vinegar

1 egg yolk

150ml (1/4 pint) sunflower oil

Salt

Black pepper

2 tbsps chopped fresh dill **or** 1 tbsp dried

**1.** Cut the fins off the fish and split it along the backbone. Remove it and all the tiny bones, too.

**2.** Mix the pickling ingredients in a bowl.

**3.** Lay the two fillets skin side down on the worktop. Spread them with the mixture and then sandwich them together, skin on top.

**4.** Cover with a double thickness of foil or clingwrap and place in a dish, weighing it down. Leave in the fridge for a minimum of three days and a maximum of five. Drain off the liquid and half-freeze, ready for easy slicing.

**5.** Whisk the mustard, sugar, vinegar and egg yolk together with a wire whisk Add the oil, whisking well. Add the seasoning and stir in the dill.

**6.** Remove the gravadlax from the freezer and slice at an angle to the skin, so that each slice is bordered with the dill. Serve with the sauce, some fresh dill and a slice of lemon or lime to garnish.

❝ We'll get this straicht richt fae the start. This is an economical dish, this. I dinna see ony pint wastin gweed siller pittin stuff ower the back o' yer throat. Value for money's fit ye're needin, I aye think. So this is a rare wye for usin up a puckle tatties. If ye'll tak a tip fae a professional, go in by the butcher and say ye're needin a suppie mince for the cat. He'll shove a lotta decent stuff at ye; stuff that a cat widna appreciate. Now ye're really savin money. Watch yersel in the middle fan ye turn up the oven because if ye dinna keep an eye on it the hale lot'll get crematit.

Ye can try it wi corned beef instead o' mince, bit corned beef's an affa price. It's dampt near a luxury nooadays, and I mind fan ye could hardly get nithing else and we were a' sick o' the sicht o' the stuff. Am I richt? Onywye, ye can leave oot the cinnamon and a' that nonsense if ye like, bit it fairly kittles up the taste. I believe some folk says it reminds them o' their holidays in Greece. Cook this and ye need nivver think o' gaun til Greece. There ye go, I've saved ye mair siller already.

# Ebenezer Grip's
# TATTIE MINCE PIE

*(Serves 4)*

**Ingredients**
50g (2oz) margarine or butter
1 tbsp cooking oil
1 onion, chopped
450g (1lb) steak mince
225g (8oz) carrots, chopped finely
2 heaped tsp tomato puree
1 tsp plain flour
2 tbsps water
pinch of dried thyme *or* 1 tsp cinnamon
Salt and pepper to taste
900g (2lb) potatoes, peeled and cut into 3mm ($\frac{1}{8}$in) slices

**Oven**
190C  375F  Gas 5

**1.** Heat 15g ($\frac{1}{2}$oz) margarine or butter and the oil in a frying pan.
Lightly brown the onion and the mince. Add the carrots and the tomato puree.

**2.** Sprinkle in the flour and mix well. Add the water, thyme or cinnamon and seasoning.

**3.** Remove from the heat and transfer the mixture into a shallow oven-proof dish

**4.** Layer the potato slices over the top, overlapping. Sprinkle with salt and pepper and dot with the remaining margarine or butter. Cover with tinfoil.

**5.** Bake in the preheated oven for 45-50 minutes until the potatoes are almost cooked. Remove foil and cook for a further 10 to 15 minutes, until the potatoes are brown.

66 This is a bit o' a swick really. Fan the editor boy o' this book came and says: "Erchie," he says, "I'm needin a recipe fae ye. For the third book." I says til him, I says: "Anither recipe? Ye've hid twa aff me already, Fit are ye deein wi a' this recipes?" Atween you and me, he's got a bit o' a brass neck, the chiel.

"I dinna dee a lotta cookin, ye see. If it's nae oot o' a tin or a bottle, ye can keep it. So I phoned ma dother-in-law at Portsoy — her that keeps the boardin-hoose — and this is fit she came up wi.

I wisna affa keen on it masel. A' that ficherin aboot wi cream and hen's breists fan ye could be doon at the pubbie haein a news and a game o' doms.

And then she telt me there wis a suppie whisky in it. What a rare quine. And I can fairly confirm that the whisky maks a' the difference. I widna hae my chucken ony ither wye, noo.

Dinna overdee the whisky, though. Jist twa tablespeens is enough. Ye wint some leftovers. And if ye've ony leftovers left over, ye ken far I am.

94

# Erchie Sotter's
# GINGERED WHISKY CHICKEN

*(Serves 4)*

**Ingredients**
30ml (2tbsp) cooking oil
25g (1oz) butter
Four chicken supremes
One onion, sliced
1in piece of fresh ginger
2 tbsps whisky
150—300ml ($^1/_4$—$^1/_2$) pint cream
1 tbsp cornflour

**Oven**
180C  350F  Gas 4

1. Heat the oil and the butter in a large frying pan.
2. Soften the onion and ginger. Remove into a flameproof casserole.
3. Brown the chicken pieces and put them into a casserole.
4. Pour the whisky into the frying-pan juices. Flame it.
5. When the flames have died down, add the chicken stock, stir well and transfer to the casserole.
6. Cover and bake for 35 minutes in the oven.
7. Mix the cornflour with a little of the cream, then add the rest.
8. Stir in the cornflour-and-cream mixture to the casserole and cook for a further 10 minutes.

6 6 This is the sort o' a recipe that my mither aye ca'ed "a kirn". I fairly agree it's a steer-up, bit what a richt fine-tastit steer-up. And Gibby raves aboot it. He's aye likit something substantial for his tea, Gibby.

The thing I like aboot it is that it's quick, and although I've got a richt lang list o' ingredients here, ye can throw in jist aboot onything, really. Jist fitivver ye hiv handy. The only thing I wid say is dinna miss oot the soy sauce, because if ye miss it oot ye miss oot the hale base o' the dish. It wid be a bittie like tryin makkin skirlie athoot ingins, ken fit I mean?

Ye can mak this wi chicken, as weel, although I aye think ye dinna get the same texture if ye try it wi chicken. And ye need a bittie texture, divn't ye? Eh? I believe the wifie Barrington-Graham tries it wi quail, bit that's her lookoot. Neena my business.

This is specially good efter Christmas or New Year fin ye've turkey for usin up. What economical it is at times lik that. Jist ae tinna pineapple chunks and ye're road-it. And if I'm feelin adventurous whiles, I likes a tattie through it. Please yersel.

# Flo Spurtle's
# TURKEY STIR-FRY

*(Serves 4)*

**Ingredients**

2 tbsps soy sauce

1 tsp honey

A small clove of garlic, crushed

750g (1½ lbs) turkey meat, cut into thin strips

225g (8oz) tinned pineapple chunks in natural juice

2 tsps cornflour

1 tbsp corn or sunflower oil

½ tsp ground cumin or curry powder

225g (8oz) courgettes, sliced

100g (4oz) mangetout

A red pepper, deseeded and sliced

Five spring onions, chopped

**1.** Combine 1 tbsp soy sauce with the honey in a glass bowl and stir in the turkey. Let it stand for 15 minutes minimum

**2.** Drain the pineapple, reserving the juice. Make it up to 8 fl oz / 200ml with water. Blend a little of this mixture with the cornflour, then add the remainder and the rest of the soy sauce.

**3.** Heat the oil in a large frying pan or wok over medium heat. Brown the garlic and heat the cumin or curry powder, stirring all the while.

**4.** Add the turkey and cook for 2-3 minutes.

**5.** Add the prepared vegetables and pineapple and cook for another two minutes, stirring all the time, until the vegetables are cooked to crisp.

**6.** Stir the pineapple-juice mixture into the pan and cook until the mixture boils and thickens.

**7.** Serve immediately with boiled rice and garnish with spring-onion tassels.

**❝**I'D THAT book-editor boy roon at ma door again the ither nicht. A dampt nuisance that laddie's turnin. 'I'm needin anither recipe fae ye, Mrs Dreep,' he says. 'Fit aboot anither poodin? Ye've got smashin poodins.' He's a saft-soapin kinna laddie.

So we newsed aboot it for a whilie on the doorstep (I widna hae him in the hoose. No thank-you) and he says that his faither's favourite poodin is meringues and cream and fruit, so I jist kent the very thing for the book And here it is — pavlova.

Dinna bother wi shop-bocht meringue cases. They're far ower white and they're like aetin polystyrene. A richt pavlova case should be fawny-coloured and it should be soft inside; the kinna soft that clogs up yer false teeth. Vinegar's the secret. Dinna mak a meringue athoot vinegar. And dinna fash yersel if it cracks. The thing's supposed ti crack. Ye've failed if it hisna crackit.

I use straaberries and mint leaves for decoration, but ye can use onything. In Australia, far this recipe startit, they use kiwis. Funny folk, Australians.

# Aggie Dreep's
# PAVLOVA

*(Serves 8)*

## Ingredients
4 egg whites
225g (8oz) caster sugar
1 tsp vanilla essence
1 tsp vinegar
2 tsps cornflour, sifted
450ml (15 fl oz) whipping cream, whipped
Fruit for the top

## Oven
150C 300F Gas 2

**1.** Mark a 23cm (9in) circle on a sheet of non-stick baking parchment and place on a baking sheet.

**2.** Whisk the egg whites in a large bowl until they are stiff.

**3.** Continue whisking and add the sugar a tablespoonful at a time. The mixture will become thick and glossy.

**4.** Fold in the vanilla essence, vinegar and cornflour.

**5.** Spoon the mixture on to the prepared marked circle, making a shallow well in the centre.

**6.** Bake in the pre-heated oven for one hour. Cool and remove paper. Transfer carefully on to a serving plate.

**7.** Just before serving, fill with the whipped cream and decorate with the fruit of your choice.

66 One of the things we teach the children at school is the importance of a good diet. When we teachers hear of the sort of things children nowadays are eating we fear for the future, I can tell you.

The problem is that children think healthy food is always boring food. If it's not fried or covered in chocolate, they think they won't like it. Well, *no, no, no* is all I have to say to that. Some of the most delicious things are also among the most nutritious.

Did you know that just one kiwifruit is so rich in vitamins that it provides all the Vitamin C an adult needs in a day? It's quite true. Those little hairy marvels from New Zealand are so packed full of goodness that half a dozen would keep you awake all night.

Recipes using kiwifruit are few and far between, sadly, but this is one of my favourites, especially on a hot summer's day or before the turkey at Christmas.

This recipe is very versatile. It can be used as a starter or as a dessert, or as an entremat (a course between courses, you know). You can also substitute just about any fruit for kiwifruit if you want to ring the changes. And it's so*ooooooo* simple.

# Euphemia Pink's
# **KIWIFRUIT SORBET**

*(Serves 6)*

### Ingredients
50g (2oz) granulated sugar

150ml ($^{1}$/$_{4}$pt) water

Six large ripe kiwifruit

15ml (1tbsp) lemon juice

30ml (2tbsps) Cointreau or Grand Marnier

Two egg whites

**1.** Put the sugar and water in a pan.

**2.** Heat gently until the sugar dissolves then bring to the boil and simmer for about 5 minutes until the mixture is syrupy. Leave to cool.

**3.** Peel the kiwifruit and liquidise or process (or mash with a potato masher in a bowl).

**4.** Add the lemon juice, liqueur and cold sugar syrup to the pulp and incorporate. Alternatively, whizz it again in the liquidiser or processor.

**5.** Pour it into a freezer container and half-freeze. Remove from the freezer and mash with a fork or potato masher.

**6.** In another bowl, whisk the egg whites until they are stiff.

**7.** Fold into the fruit mixture, making sure everything is blended.

**8.** Return to the freezer for another two or three hours until just firm.

**9.** Serve in scoops in individual glass dishes with a strawberry to decorate.

" This is one o' those recipes that yer mither disna like and so she winna let ye hae it. If ye play yer cards richt, though, yer faither'll get a taste for it and then it'll be twa against one.

My mither says this spiles a good fruit salad, and she says we should be eatin really healthy nooadays because wir life depends on it. I think that's gey funny comin fae a wifie that sits in front o' the TV eatin pandrops and chocolate creams ivry nicht, bit ye canna tell parents, can ye?

The great thing aboot this fruit salad, according til ma teacher, Miss Pink, is that there's nae fruit syrup near it. And nae fruit syrup equals nae extra calories. And nae extra calories means nae lumps and bumps roon aboot yer tum-tum.

The toffee-sauce recipe came fae my Auntie at Cornhill. She maks up a batch ivry wikk. She says that as lang as ye keep it in the fridge, it'll keep jist lovely. She says they've had some a hale wikk efter it wis made and it wis as if it wis jist new oot o' the pan. I canna say if that's true or no; I've nivver been able to keep it a wikk.

# Wayne Spurtle's
# **TOFFEE-SAUCE FRUIT SALAD**

*(Serves 4)*

**Ingredients**
Five oranges
450g (1lb) strawberries, hulled and halved, if necessary
Two large bananas, sliced
25g (1oz) chopped nuts, toasted (optional)

**Sauce**
125g (4oz) butter
125g (4oz) soft light brown sugar
300ml ($^1/_2$pint) single cream
A few drops of vanilla essence

**1.** Place the butter, sugar and cream in a pan and heat gently until the sugar has dissolved. Stir all the time.

**2.** Increase the heat and boil for five minutes.

**3.** Stir in the vanilla essence and allow to cool.

**4.** Squeeze the juice from one of the oranges and skin and segment the four others.

**5.** Place all the prepared fruit in individual serving dishes and add the juice.

**6.** Stir gently and top with half of the toffee sauce and chopped nuts, if you are using nuts.

*(The rest of the toffee sauce will keep in a screw top jar*
*in the fridge for several days, if you can resist it)*

6 6 I've tried a lotta cheesecakes in
ma time. I've tried them oot o'
bakers; I've tried them oot o'
freezers in shops; I've tried them in
caffys, and I've tried them in funcy
restaurants. And I can say athoot
fear o' contermation that I hinna
found a cheesecake yet that's
worth ca'in a cheesecake.

Div you nae find the same?
They're either as licht that there's
nithing til them. They're mair caul
sooflies. Or they're as heavy that
twa bites and ye're stappit and ye've
the taste left in ye for days.

This is the recipe that'll change yer mind
aboot cheesecakes, I guarantee. Dinna be put
aff by the gelatine; I ken a lotta folk thinks usin
gelatine's affa difficult, bit it's nae mair difficult than onything else; tak it fae me. Ye
can go for that packet cream cheese if ye like, bit I prefers a low-fat soft cheese fae
the delicatessen coonter at the supermarket. It disna taste ower satty, and fa wints a
satty cheesecake.

Finally, ye can decorate this cheesecake wi onything ye like. I find mandarins are
fine and snappy. Or goosers. Or strawberries. Or blackcurrants. Onything, really.

# Geneva Brose's
# STRONACH CHEESECAKE

*(Serves 6)*

**Ingredients**
75g (3oz) butter
90ml (6tbsp) golden syrup
150g (5oz) plain flour
5ml (1 level tsp) cornflour
1 egg, beaten
1 large lemon
150ml (¼ pint) milk
10ml (2 level tsps) powdered gelatine
225g (8oz) cream cheese
150ml (¼ pint) double cream, whipped

**Oven**
170C 325F Gas 3

**1.** Grease a 18cm (7in) springform tin.
**2.** Cream fat and 30ml ( two level tbsps) syrup. Mix in the flour. Spread over the base of the tin and bake for about 30 minutes until pale brown. Leave to cool.
**3.** Blend the cornflour with the egg. Add the grated lemon rind.
**4.** Boil the milk. Stir gradually into the cornflour mixture. Return to the pan and stir over a low heat until thickened. Cool.
**5.** Dissolve the gelatine in 30 ml (2 tbsps) lemon juice.
**6.** Whisk the cream cheese with the remaining syrup. Continue whisking and add in the cold custard and gelatine.
**7.** Stir in half the cream. Pour over the base and chill.
**8.** Release from the tin and decorate with the remaining cream
**9.** Whisk egg whites until they are stiff. Fold in using a metal spoon.
**10.** Put the mixture into the cold biscuit base and leave to set.
**11.** Release from the tin and decorate with remaining cream.

66 The North-east housewife that canna mak a pancake is nae worth ca'in a housewife. That's my opinion. It's nae as if there's ony mystery til it. A pancake is one o' the simplest things. Steer up yer stuff, drap it on yer girdle, turn them ower and cover them wi a cloot. Twinty minutes fae start ti finish. Fit could be simpler.?

The editor boy fae this book said that I should include hints and tips so that you folk widna get lost, but fit hints and tips is there? A bloomin eediot could folly this.

I will say that the syrup maks a' the difference. I've tried pancakes wi syrup, and I've tried pancakes athoot, and I can definitely say that the pancakes wi the syrup turns a better colour and they seem a bittie mair moist, though they dinna keep the same, I find. If ye're a hungry femly they winna keep lang fitivver; I wid glory on wi the syrup, if I wis you.

Ye hear a lotta folk ca'in pancakes bannocks. Well, as far as I ken, they're nae nithing o' the sort bannocks. Bannocks is that great big thin things that English folk toss on Shrove Tuesday. Pancakes is fit this is. (Or is it the ither wye aboot? I forget).

Save a lotta trouble and ca them Drop Scones.

# Dorothy Birze's
# PANCAKES (DROP SCONES)

**Ingredients**

450g (1lb) self-raising flour

75g (3oz) sugar

$^1/_2$ tsp salt

2 tbsps golden syrup (spoon dipped in boiling water first)

300ml ($^1/_2$pint) milk

Two eggs, beaten

**1.** Put the dry ingredients and the syrup into a mixing bowl

**2.** Beat the milk with the eggs.

**3.** Add the egg-milk mixture to the dry ingredients and syrup and beat well, until the result is the dropping consistency of thick cream.

**4.** Heat the griddle or a heavy frying pan and grease it very lightly, removing the surplus with kitchen roll.

**5.** Take a tablespoon of the mixture and drop it into the pan. You should manage to do four at a time, if they are well spaced out.

**6.** When bubbles start to appear, turn them over and cook the other side.

**7.** Place them to cool in a clean tea-towel, covering them up between times.

❝ Ye should really start makkin this fruity tea loaf the day afore ye need it. Ye can start in the mornin if ye like, bit ye winna get nearly sic a moist and tasty loaf.

This is a great favourite at the sales o' work in the village hall, especially wi auler folk that minds fine on aul-fashioned bakin. I'll often see a pensioner approachin the sales table and sayin: "Hiv ye ony mair o' Virginia's fruity tea loaf?" I ken I shouldna blaa ma ain trumpet, bit there ye go. And fin they find oot that a' the tea-loaves wis selt a lang time ago, ye can see their shooders sinkin and their little lippies wobblin. Ye feel that sorry for them.

Some folk prefers this loafie athoot the spice, bit I think a fruity loaf athoot a bittie spice is like scrambled eggs athoot toast — there's something missin. Ye can dee athoot the raisins, though. I find dried fruit's an affa price nooadays, so I tried an experiment; I made it athoot the raisins and it came oot richt bonnie. It didna keep the same, mind you, bit it wis richt fine-tastit.

Servin suggestions? Ye can eat it dry, bit a bittie butter or jam jist sets it aff.

# Virginia Huffie's
# FRUITY TEA BREAD

**Ingredients**

200g (7oz)  mixed dried fruit or use just raisins

450ml (³/₄pt) warm tea

200g (7oz) soft brown sugar

275g (10 oz) self-raising flour

1 teaspoon mixed spice

1 egg, beaten

**Oven**

160C   325F   Gas 3

**1.** Put the fruit in a bowl and cover with the tea the night before. It will plump up beautifully.

**2.** Grease a loaf tin with margarine and place greaseproof paper in the bottom.

**3.** Sift the flour into another bowl and stir in the sugar and mixed spice.

**4.** Make a well in the middle and pour into this the fruit mixture and the beaten egg. Stir well to incorporate, but don't beat.

**5.** Pour the mixture into the loaf tin and bake for 1³/₄ hours. If the top is becoming too brown, cover it with greaseproof paper and lower the heat.

66 It's sooooo nice to be back with you all again and to be sharing this time together. When I was asked for a recipe for the book I couldn't think of anything better than simnel cake. It has such significance for me, and it's tasty, too.

I'll admit that it takes quite a time to prepare, but I do assure you, ladies and gentlemen, that the time and effort you expend will be well rewarded with the grateful looks on all those happy and surprised faces.

Your only problem will arise if you don't like marzipan, as this recipe rather depends on it, I'm afraid. Making a simnel cake when you don't like marzipan would be a bit like asking a vegetarian to fry up a steak, I suppose. Ha, ha, ha.

People often ask me at the Kirk Social is there is a significance to the fact that there must be exactly 11 marzipan balls round the perimeter of the cake as decoration. I tell them it's in memory of Aberdeen Football Club. Ha, ha. Just my little whimsy.

No, the 11 marzipan balls represent the 11 Apostles at the Last Supper who were the decent chaps. There you go; confection and edification in one fell swoop.

# The Rev. Montgomery Thole's
# SIMNEL CAKE

### Ingredients
225g (8oz) softened butter
225g (8oz) dark brown soft sugar
Four Size 3 eggs
275g (10oz) plain flour, sieved
15ml (1tbsp) black treacle
5ml (1tsp) ground cinnamon
Grated rind of one small orange
30ml (2tbsps) brandy
575g (1$^{1}/_{4}$lb) mixed dried fruit
900g (2lb) white marzipan
45ml (3tbsps) golden syrup

### Oven
150C  300F  Gas 2

**1.** Grease a 20.5cm / 8in round cake tin and line with greaseproof paper.

**2.** Cream butter and sugar. Beat in eggs one at a time, adding a little flour after each one. Stir in the treacle, the rest of the flour, cinnamon, orange rind, brandy and fruit.

**3.** Spoon half the mixture into the tin.

**4.** Roll out a third of the marzipan to an 8in round and lay over the mixture in the tin. Spoon the rest of the mixture into the tin and it level off.

**5.** Bake in the preheated oven for 2$^{1}/_{2}$ — 2$^{3}/_{4}$ hours, until a skewer comes out cleanly. Cool in the tin for 15 minutes, then turn the cake out on to a wire rack to cool.

**6.** Place cake on a serving plate.

**7** Heat the syrup and brush the cake with some of it.

**8.** Roll out another third of the marzipan and cover the top of the cake. (You might like to scallop the edges to make it look pretty.)

**9.** Form the remaining marzipan into 11 balls and arrange around the top of the cake. Brush the top of the cake with the remaining syrup and brown under a hot grill.

That's it for yet another year. We hope you have enjoyed your short stay in the village of Stronach and that you have found something to amuse you, inform you or just fatten you up.

Stronach publications are available from all good bookshops and newsagents. In case of difficulty, write to us, enclosing a cheque payable to Stronach Media Ltd. We will dispatch the goods post-free within the United Kingdom. Dispatch abroad will be charged at cost; please write for current rates.

| | |
|---|---|
| Stronach Volume One | £7.95 |
| Stronach Volume Two | £7.95 |
| Stronach Volume Three | £7.95 |
| The Stronach Tapes (three hours of stories on two audio-cassettes) | £7.95 |

Write to:

**Alison Reid, Stronach Media Ltd., Tullynessle, Alford, Aberdeenshire, AB33 8QN**

**And congratulations to the winners of the 1994 Stronach Mastermind Competition:**

First:      Helen Noble, Peterhead.

Second:    Ian Davidson, Fort William.
Brenda Keir, Dundee.

Third:      Frances McDonald, Insch.